Prepare to shit your pants...

Viz

D0229941

THE
TURTLE'S HEAD

A steaming stool stuffed with the stinkiest bits of issues 64 to 69

"A comedy arsequake registering 10 on the sphincter scale"

The late Dr. Magnus Pike

Edited by Chris Donald

Written and illustrated by
Chris Donald, Graham Dury, Simon Donald and Simon Thorp

Oh, and Davey Jones. And John Fardell

And with other bits by Lew Stringer, Simon Ecob and Graham Murdoch

Photography by Colin Davison

IBS No. 1870 870 840

Published in Great Britain by John Brown Publishing Limited,
The Old Ropehouse, Crabtree Lane, Fulham, London SW6 6LU.

First printed September 1996

5

WE HAVEN'T WON T

Hitler fights on

War Ministry files recently made public under the Freedom of Information Act reveal a shocking legacy left by Hitler which could yet reverse the result of the second world war, according, as usual, to a BBC children's TV presenter.

The record books show that officially England won the war in 1945. But evidence now coming to light suggests that Hitler's last card – played in his Berlin bunker in the final hours before his suicide – may have been an ace.

MORRIS

This is the view of former 'Animal Magic' presenter Johnny Morris. For he believes the Fuhrer and his evil Nazi cohorts left a time bomb ticking underneath England way after their deaths. An evolutionary time bomb which is now set to explode.

DIRTY

Adolf Hitler was barely out of nappies when the eminent scientist Charles Darwin first published his book 'The Theory of Evolution'. In it he explained how man evolved from fish, who crawled out of the sea and turned into monkeys. Previously it had been thought that man evolved from a snake and an apple in the Garden of Eden.

FLASH

Morris believes that during the latter years of the war Hitler's top Nazi scientists invented a bomb which would actually cause evolution to go backwards. The top secret device was thought to have been destroyed during the allied invasion of Berlin. However, papers just published reveal that the bomb may have been flown to Britain by Rudolf Hess, and hidden in a field near Ipswich.

Nazi scientists set to have the last laugh

Contemporary thinking now suggests that as the allied armies marched on Berlin, a desperate Hitler pressed a special red button in his bunker which triggered the evolutionary time bomb. And scientists now fear that since that moment in May 1945 evolution in Britain has been going steadily backwards, while it continues to go forwards in the rest of the world.

BREAK

If the worst fears are confirmed, within five years everyone in Britain will have turned into a monkey. And by the year 2000 the entire population of England, Wales and Scotland will have evolved into fish which will flap about a bit before crawling into the sea, never to be seen again.

ACCELERATOR

Morris points to a catalogue of crucial evidence which he claims proves his theory beyond all reasonable doubt:

Bananas. Or is it? Johnny Morris points to this fruit as evidence that Hitler is turning us into a nation of monkeys.

- In the ten years immediately after the war banana sales in Britain escalated, from virtually nil in 1945, to lots in 1955. Today, UK banana sales are at an all-time record high.

- Over the 48 year period since the cessation of hostilities table manners in Britain have declined gradually to the point where virtually nobody uses a knife and fork properly anymore.

- In Britain men's bodies are showing greater signs of hair growth. Sean Connery and Peter Sellers for example, both having hairy backs.

- Germans make better cars than us. And so do the Japanese.

Ironically, Morris is convinced that Hitler's original plan was not to turn us all into fish. As he explains.

CLUTCH

"I believe Hitler planned to conquer Britain by de-evolutionising us all into monkeys so that he could march into London unopposed. He then planned to offer us the secret of man's red fire, in return for the keys to Buckingham Palace. It was a brilliant plan, and if it had worked Hitler would have been crowned King of England."

However, the Nazi scientists misjudged the strength of bomb required, and Hitler unknowingly triggered an unstoppable evolutionary disaster by detonating his secret weapon.

STEERING

We rang Germany and asked a spokesman to comment on these allegations, however he denied the existence of the so-called evolutionary time bomb. "This sounds like sour grapes to me. I wouldn't be surprised if Mr Morris is simply miffed because, since winning the World Cup in 1966, England have singularly failed to establish themselves as a force in world football," he said, "whilst Germany have consistently dominated at international level. Perhaps you should ask Mr Morris whether he will be going to watch the World Cup Finals in America this summer. I will, because of course we qualified."

WHEEL

When we rang former England manager Graham Taylor for a comment on Mr Morris's theory his wife told us he was busy in the garden. "Try ringing back at tea-time. You may well catch him then" she said.

'Ladies and gentlemen, Mr Elton John...' Could pop stars like George Michael and Elton John look like this in 5 years time?

IT'S A LITTLE 'PARKIE' OUT HERE THIS MORNING.

'APPEN MY NEXT GUEST IS GEOFFREY BOYCOTT

HE WAR YET!
from the grave

Evolution: Was Darwin right?

It seems hard to imagine that hundreds of years ago we were all fish in the sea. But that is exactly what scientists would have us believe.

So how else might we explain the evolution of mankind? Are there any new theories which may in time supersede Darwin's best seller? We decided to ask a few stars from the world of popular music whether they would share their own personal views with us.

Baby faced **Cliff Richard** seems to have defied science ever since the day he was born by retaining his youthful looks (and not going all thin and leathery as you would expect). Perhaps that is because he looks to God and not science for life's answers.

We ask the stars

to crawl out of the sea easily and perhaps even begin to climb trees" he told us.

Sammy Davis Junior was only too keen to expound his own views despite dying of cancer. The all-time great singer, dancer, musician, comedian and actor believes that evolution doesn't stop at man, and he suggests that Darwin should publish a revised edition of his theory. "If you look

"I'm sticking to the Bible's version of events", Cliff told us. "Some people may find it hard to swallow the Adam and Eve story, but I do. You can't beat a good yarn".

George Michael, recently at odds with his record company, is also at odds with Charles Darwin on the subject of evolution. "I really can't see how a fish is going to crawl out of the sea and spend hundreds of years turning into a monkey without being eaten by a seagull", said the heart-throb singer. "My money is on space aliens having landed on Earth, killed all the dinosaurs, and then left everything wide open for the monkeys to take over".

Former school teacher **Sting** spoke with some authority on the subject. "Darwin's theory is much more far reaching than anyone has yet acknowledged in this article." he told us. "However, if I were asked to improve on it I would suggest that rather than man evolving from fish and monkeys, they perhaps first turned into sort of crabs which would have enabled them

around you man may rule the Earth, but certain species like dolphins and ants may be angling to take over. Dolphins can already talk, and if they were to evolve out of the sea we could have our hands full. Ants are also ones to watch. If they got bigger, and discovered fire and the wheel, they could be running the show within a few years, if not months even."

Do you have a theory of evolution? If so, write and let us know what it is. We'll be asking a top scientist – or that bloke on the car adverts who used to do Tomorrow's World – to choose the winner. And first prize will be £250's worth of record vouchers, plus an Indian meal for two, and a couple of garden chairs.

Your theory must be typed, and no longer than a single page. Send it to Viz Theories of Evolution Competition, P.O. Box 1PT, Newcastle upon Tyne NE99 1PT. All theories must be received by no later than March 1st 1994. The winner will be announced in our April issue, No. 65.

CATCH A FISHY STAR
(AND PUT IT IN YOUR POCKET)

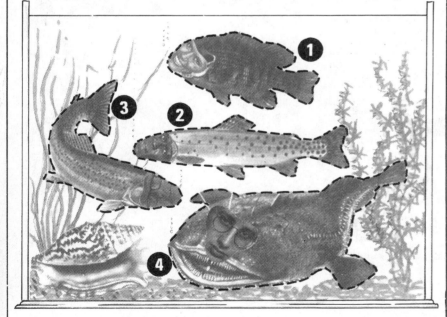

Try to imagine what your favourite stars would look like if they had evolved backwards into fish. Difficult, isn't it. Well, here's a game that will help you. In this fish tank there are four top

celebrities who we have cleverly disguised in fish form. Can you recognise them?

For extra fun, try cutting out your four fish stars, and attaching a paper

clip to each one. Put them in a bucket, then, kneeling on a chair dangle a magnet on the end of a piece of string into the bucket and see how many stars you can catch!

ANSWERS: The fish stars are: Fish 1. Anneka Rice, Fish 2. Frank Bruno, Fish 3. Chris Evans and Fish 4. Rob Newman

LETTERBOCKS
Viz, P.O.Box 1PT
Newcastle upon Tyne
NE99 1PT

'Scope for an improvement

I find it quite sickening to see billions of dollars being spent on this so-called 'Hubble space telescope', when the best it can possibly achieve is to send back yet more blurred and boring pictures which don't even look like space. Surely for a fraction of the cost these scientists could come up with a telescope that could see through Catherine Zeta-Jones' bedroom window. It would be far cheaper to maintain, and at last we'd have some pictures worth looking at.

A. Peppercorn
York

Now that the AA is advertising itself as the 'fourth emergency service', perhaps we can look forward to a TV drama like Casualty, The Bill or London's Burning. Stranded motorists wait on the hard shoulder for five hours until a spotty youth in a van with disco lights on the top arrives. Then he tows them to a garage for a £150 service simply because they've run out of petrol. I'm sure it would be popular viewing.

R.A. Coates
Blackpool

Isn't it about time the rest of the UK recognised the great contribution that Birmingham has made to the cultural life of our country. Where would we be without Heavy Metal music, Crossroads and Jasper Carrott?

B. Inkster
Middlesex

What do you think of Birmingham? Do you think it's great or do you think it's crap? Do you think your town is better? If you do, write and tell us why. Write to 'Better than Birmingham' at our usual Letterbocks address. There's a twelve inch ruler for the sender of the best letter, and a road map of the Exeter area for the runner-up.

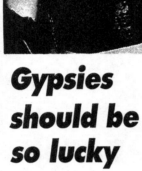

Gypsies should be so lucky

If the heather that these so-called Gypsies sell is so lucky, how come, despite having bunches of it themselves, they're reduced to flogging it in the streets to earn a few bob?

G. Ivatt
Derby

I think bank managers should be given similar powers to those enjoyed by head school teachers. I doubt whether quite so many customers would allow their accounts to go into the red if the threat of detention or lines was hanging over their head.

V. Dougleby
Barclays Bank
Fulchester

How come ugly bastard MPs always seem to pull the birds, while a decent looking bloke like me never gets anything on the side? John Major talks about making Britain a 'fairer society'. Well, the first step would be for the Government to stop hogging all the dirty women, and give Joe Public a look in for a change.

G. Clark
Magaluff, nr. Hull

It's no wonder that G. Clark (Letterbocks, this page) isn't getting his leg over. All the birds in Hull are boilers.

J. Holden
Sheffield

Instead of writing to Letterbocks why don't sex starved squaddies drop us a line instead? We are two Cindy Crawford lookalikes who would appreciate photos from any single, heterosexual soldiers serving in Bosnia, Belize, Northern Ireland or anywhere else, preferably over 21, and at least 3 feet tall. No perverts please.

Angelina & Vicki
Calle Salitre, No. 19, 7a
Malaga 29002
SPAIN

Wig bank mix-up

I'm dyslexic, and your recent 'Wig Amnesty' caused me some embarrassment, I can tell you! I went to drop my wig into a 'wig bank', but got confused and had a 'big wank' in the newsagents shop instead. Do I win £5?

W. Spooner
Ism

I am worried about my son. The other night he said he was going out with some friends to paint the town red. The following morning he awoke complaining of a dreadful headache and was unable to go to college. I wonder whether perhaps this could have been caused by the paint fumes?

Mrs P. Brown
Shrewsbury

Gloves to finger villians

If burglars wear gloves to disguise their fingerprints, why oh why can't the glove manufacturers make gloves with their own individual 'fingerprints'. This would enable police to identify the gloves used, and then trace the criminals by checking through credit card details of all glove purchases.

I. Mansell
Brighton

Whilst in Germany recently I think I discovered the street where Johnny Fartpant's cousin lives. Do I win £5?

Joan Differ
Glasgow

After my insurance company suggested I have my car registration number etched onto the windows I took their advice. In fact I went one step further, and had it etched onto the windows of my house as well. Some deterrent that proved to be. Two days later I arrived home to find one of the windows had been smashed, and my house had been ransacked by burglars. So much for the insurance companies. They're only interested in one thing. Money.

J. Gresly
Doncaster

I recently had first hand experience of the strange phenomenon known as 'spontaneous human combustion'. I had always been sceptical about this sort of thing until my brother-in-law burst into flames the other day whilst reading a newspaper. I was sitting right beside him at the time yet I have no idea what caused him to suddenly explode into a fireball. Luckily my wife was alert enough to take these remarkable photographs. I wonder whether any other readers had similar experiences?

L. Houston
Whyteleafe, Surrey

*Have any other readers experienced this bizarre phenomenon? We'll pay £20 for any similar remarkable photographs which we publish. (Please note: Readers should follow Mr Houston's example and take their furniture to a safe place outdoors before setting it alight.)

Check out my idea

The other day at the supermarket the check-out girl handed me a list of my shopping along with my change. Surely it would make more sense for them to hand housewives this list *before* we do our shopping, thus saving us the bother of having to write a shopping list.

Mrs G. Stephenson
Newcastle upon Tyne

In reply to Nick and Ian's letter (Letterbocks, issue 63), if they're so fucking bright why are they flogging record players for a living in a poxy hi-fi shop in Cornwall? When we've finished browsing around your shop us students go and get *proper* jobs, like solicitors and bank managers. And if we want a record player, we certainly don't go to Cornwall to buy it.

Elaine Vicars
Truro

MIX luminous paint with your dog food to help prevent unfortunate pedestrians treading on dog turds during the dark winter evenings.
Simon Mellishoe
Redhill

RE-KINDLE memories of your summer holidays in sunny Greece by turning off your water supply, removing all toilet roll from your bathroom, placing a dirty bucket next to your toilet and forcing some Plasticine up behind your index finger nail.
Richard Buttock
Thurrock

SAVE money by arranging your dirty dishes on your roof rack before visiting the car wash.
R. Maunsell
Southampton

MARRIED COUPLES. Avoid damage to your doors by attaching a balloon to the top of the door frame before starting a row. Then, when you storm out of the room, closing the door gently will have the same dramatic effect as a violent slam, without causing any damage to the door.
O. Stacey
Essex

SCABS with tufts of fur attached removed from your cat make ideal fishing flies.
D.T.
Cardiff

SAVE more money by filling your boot with dirty washing and then leaving it open next time you visit the car wash.
R. Maunsell
Southampton

ALWAYS keep tubes of haemorrhoid ointment and Deep Heat rub well separated in your bathroom cabinet.
P. Turner
Liverpool

SPECTACLE wearers. Clean your glasses free of charge by sellotaping them to the radiator grille next time you visit the car wash.
R. Maunsell
Southampton

PRETEND to live in a hard water area by placing finely ground pieces of egg shell in the bottom of your kettle.
A. J. Hill
Grantham

HI-FI enthusiasts. Clean the inside of your CD player by dipping your CDs in hot sudsy water and then playing them immediately. As they spin the water will be sprayed throughout the CD console. Repeat with cold water to rinse.
Chip Rowe
Washington DC, USA

PENSIONERS. Save money on heating bills this winter by recalling the moment when, at the 1992 pre-election Labour Party rally, Neil Kinnock said:

"Comrades. Alright! Alright! Well *alright!*" The thought of it will make you glow from head to foot with embarrassment.
D.T.
Cardiff

WHEN throwing somebody a sharp instrument such as a Stanley knife or bread knife, always throw it sharp end first as invariably they tend to turn whilst in the air.
W. Stanier
Cricklewood

FIND OUT what you look like when you're asleep by learning astral projection and then glancing over your shoulder just as you are leaving your body.
Steve Wright
Hornsey

MAKE shopkeepers feel like criminals and con men by carefully checking *their* change, and holding notes up to the light, before accepting them.
Alan Dodsworth
Leicester

FELLAS. Next time you're contemplating masturbation in your bedroom, make sure your bedside lamp is *between* you and the curtains, to avoid giving neighbours an entertaining 'shadow play'.
J. Holden
Swindon

Roads 'not safe for lesbians'

Outrageous TV presenter Hufty, bald headed host of Channel Four's controversial youth show The Word, is set to spearhead a new lesbian road safety initiative.

'The Hufty Club' will be a partly Government financed project aimed at reducing road fatalities among lesbian pedestrians, although the initiative for the scheme came from Hufty herself.

FAME

The Liverpool born alternative comic sprang to national fame when she succeeded in beating a host of dumb bimbos at auditions for the £200,000 a year presenter's job last year, and promptly said 'fuck' on live TV. But away from the screen, Hufty is a fervent campaigner for homosexual road safety.

GREASE

She, along with Government road safety officials, is alarmed by the appalling number of road accidents in Britain each year involving lesbians on foot. Although no official figures exist, it is believed that up to ninety per cent – that's over half – of the people injured or killed on Britain's roads each year, three out of every ten of which are pedestrians, of which as many as one in eight is a lesbian, or bisexual woman. That's a fifty per cent increase on the same figure for the previous year.

SATURDAY

The Hufty Club will be advertised on television, with Hufty herself, dressed as a rabbit, inviting fellow lesbian road users to join. Members will receive a membership card and a special Hufty badge, as well as books and leaflets which explain the safest ways to cross a road. Visits to schools are also planned, where Hufty (in her rabbit suit) will lecture children, both heterosexual and homosexual (and kids who haven't decided yet) on road safety matters. She will be accompanied by a police officer dressed as a badger.

NIGHT

A spokesman for The Word yesterday defended Hufty's decision to campaign for lesbian road safety, and denied that it would interfere with her TV work. "Do you know anyone who'd be prepared to chop their cock off and eat it on live TV?" he asked us last night. "If you do, ask them to give us a ring".

According to Hufty, the commonest mistakes made by lesbian pedestrians, or "plesbians", are:

- **STEPPING OUT** from between parked vehicles without stopping to look for cars.
- **RUNNING** out into the road from behind an ice cream van or bus.
- **CROSSING** a busy road instead of using a safe crossing place such as a subway, footbridge or pedestrian crossing.

FEVER

Hufty is not the first controversial female Channel 4 youth music TV presenter to become involved in a surreal sex orientated distortion of a sixties children road safety campaign. For

Safety campaigner Hufty yesterday

in 1985, Paula Yates, co-presenter of The Tube, campaigned unsuccessfully for a new Cycling Proficiency Test to be introduced exclusively for yo-yo knickered heterosexual girls, dirty stop-outs and slags.

11

14

CD.GPD.SD.ST. Pics by Colin D.

The Egyptians knew the secret of LONG HAIR

Now *YOU* can too with 'Pyramid' formula mystical growth

HAIR COMPOST

Your hair will simply grow and grow!

- **NO MORE BALD PATCHES!**
- **GROW THICK BLACK LOCKS OVERNIGHT!**

This million year old formula has been carved on pyramid walls and passed down through the centuries by the Egyptian mystical Kings. Now the head compost of the ancients can be yours for as little as £79.99 a sack.

WARNING Do not wear motorcycle helmet within 2 hours of compost application as rapid hair growth will occur.

APPLY DAILY TO THE TOP OF YOUR HEAD IN A DARKENED ROOM, THEN LIE DOWN WITH YOUR ARMS FOLDED FOR HALF AN HOUR. SIMPLE AS THAT. AND WITHIN MINUTES YOU WILL HAVE STRONG, THICK, HEALTHY SHOULDER LENGTH BLACK HAIR.

Send your order to: PYRAMID GROWTH LABORATORIES, c/o Park Hill Pig Farm, Faversham, Kent.

Name.................................... Address..

I desire the secret of the ancient Egyptian Kings. Please send me two sacks of Hair Compost at £79.99 each. I enclose a cheque for £200 made payable to Park Hill Pig Farm Ltd., Please keep the change.

Signed...

Turn WATER into PETROL
WITH
Petrol Fish ™
THE FISH THAT (Esso) TRIED TO BAN!

- *Fuel bills vanish overnight!*
- *Beat price increases at the PUMPS!*
- *Enjoy FREE motoring FOR LIFE!*

These rare and only recently discovered goldfish occur naturally deep beneath the Earth in the oil fields of Saudi Arabia. No larger than ordinary goldfish, and the same colour, their unique bio-chemistry gives them an unusually high octane capacity. As a result when they drink water, their urine turns into petrol. Place just one of these fish in your petrol tank then fill it with water and within seconds nature's miraculous **PETROL FISH** are turning the water into petrol. So successful is this natural fuel saving technique lawyers from all the major petrol companies have tried to ban the sale of our product. So far they have been unsuccessful, but we recommend that you ORDER TODAY while **PETROL FISH** are still legally available.

Please rush me..............*(state quantity) **PETROL FISH** @£100 each.

Name...............................Address.................................

Tick one ☐ FOUR STAR ☐ UNLEADED ☐ SUPER PLUS UNLEADED

*Sorry we regret that customers are limited to a maximum of 800 fish each.

Send orders to: PETROL FISH SALES (UK) Ltd., The Aquarium, Colchester High Street, Colchester, Essex, CO1 5AH.

You too can be a beautiful Princess with
'Mirror mirror on the wall' ™

"YOU ARE"

- ★ *LOSING YOUR LOOKS?*
- ★ *WRINKLES BEGINNING TO SHOW?*
- ★ *FED UP WITH HUBBY NOT PAYING YOU COMPLIMENTS?*

Our magic* mirror is guaranteed* to change all that. Simply pop it on your bathroom wall and ask the question "Who is the fairest of them all?" Then press a button, stand back, and within a few moments the magic* mirror will reply "YOU ARE". Genuine feau quality plastic mirror with moulded surround. Petrol driven engine delivers 24 compliments to the gallon. First time starter on cold mornings.

Send a cheque, postal order or cash to: Mirror Mirror Offer, P.O. Box 12, Basildon, Essex. Due to the quality of this product please allow an unlimited period of time for delivery.

MAGICAL MIRRORS (UK) LTD.
Manufacturers of petrol driven complimentary fairytale mirrors since 1933.

*The words 'magic' and 'guaranteed' are used in their broader sense. Please note that Mirror Mirror is neither magic, nor guaranteed.

WARNING: Keep bathroom well ventilated. Petrol driven audio mirrors can occasionally explode and should not be attached to a supporting structural wall.

ONLY £599.95

You sleep while your gloves do the driving
Home, James!
Automatic driving gloves

Faux POLICE approved!

You DRINK, your gloves DRIVE!

IF you CRASH, we return your CASH!*

*No Refunds

Ideal for:
- * **Drunk Drivers**
- * **Disqualified Drivers**
- * **Women Drivers**
- * **Andrew Ridgely**

£299.99

Name...
address...
Dates & times when I'm out................................
I do/do not have a dog (please delete)
I enclose £.........Signed................

Home, James Chauffeur Gloves come complete with 12 MONTHS FULLY COMPREHENSIVE car insurance!

Send to: Box 23, Cardiff, Wales.
Please allow a long time for delivery

19

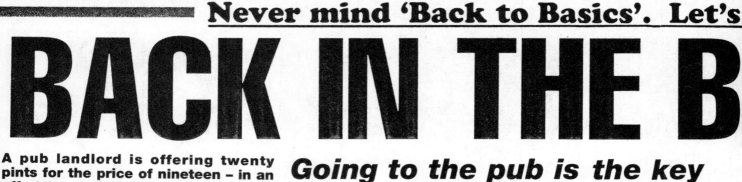

BACK IN THE B

A pub landlord is offering twenty pints for the price of nineteen – in an effort to get Britain back on the road to economic recovery.

Sid Fletcher, landlord of the Three Bulls Rings in Fulchester High Street, believes that most of Britain's social and economic problems are the result of insufficient lunchtime drinking. And he has launched a campaign aimed at getting Britain back in the boozer.

EVILS

He believes that two of today's greatest evils, high crime and unemployment, are directly attributable to people not drinking enough during midday sessions.

"If you compare this country now to how it was forty years ago, the differences are amazing. In the fifties there wasn't any crime, apart from that bloke who shot a copper on the sweet shop roof, and unemployment didn't exist. Now the streets aren't safe anymore, and there's no jobs."

LEVIS

Sid believes it's more than just coincidence that in the fifties there were hundreds

Major – 'back to basics' campaign

more pubs than there are today, and the vast majority of them were busy at lunchtimes.

ELVIS

"Nowadays pubs are usually quiet at lunchtime, with a few people coming in for a sandwich and a quick half. But I remember only too well how in the old days workers would come in from the factories and shipyards and drink ten and eleven pints in an hour. And those were the days when Britain's economy was booming."

Going to the pub is the key to Britain's success

Sid agrees with the current Government policy of 'back to basics', but he believes the most basic step of all is to get people drinking at lunchtimes. "I take hundreds of pounds every night, but I pay two barmaids to work lunchtimes and I'm lucky if there's fifty quid in the till by three o'clock." he told us. "If Mr Major wants to revive the economy he could give it one hell of a kick start by halving the price of beer between 11am and 3pm. The extra revenue that would generate in my bar alone would enable me to re-decorate the toilets and buy some new tables. And the knock-on effect would surely benefit the entire economy."

LIVES

In his attempt to lure workers out of their offices and workplaces Sid has come up with the innovative idea of giving customers twenty pints of lager for the price of nineteen, a saving of over £1.30. But there is a catch.

Boozing for Britain. A lunch-time boozer enjoys a lunch-time booze. In the boozer.

"The offer only applies if they can drink it all in an hour. It's not a lot to ask. A few years ago I had regulars in here drinking twenty pints at lunchtime, then coming back for another twenty before they went home for their tea. Nowadays people can't drink anymore. It's no wonder kids are growing up out of control, and committing crime, when parents are setting such a poor example."

---

⑩ tips on how best to behave at work after drinking 20 pints of beer at lunchtime

Unfortunately Britain's bosses aren't too keen on lunch-time boozing. But follow these ten tips and your boss need never know you've been drinking.

1. Sucking a mint will help disguise the smell of beer on your breath, but remember to buy the mints *before* you go into the pub as it may be more difficult to buy them afterwards.

2. If you have a desk job, try to spend the entire afternoon with your elbow on the desk and your head resting on your hand. Sit upright, holding a pen in your other hand. This will make you look busy, and thoughtful.

3. Do not start any conversations yourself, and if you are spoken to try to speak more slowly than you would normally do. This will counter the effect of your brain trying to speak more quickly than usual.

4. If your boss asks you a question, count to ten before your reply. Keep sentences short, stopping and counting to ten again between each sentence.

5. You may not realise it but your eyelids will naturally tend to drop. So make an extra effort to raise your eyebrows while talking.

6. Keep alert by trying to remember your postcode, and repeating it over and over in your mind.

7. Try to keep movement to a minimum. Do not walk anywhere unless it is absolutely necessary.

8. If you do have to go anywhere, to the toilet for example, choose a route which enables you to punctuate your journey by casually leaning on walls or items of fixed furniture.

9. If there is a patterned carpet in the room try following the pattern to enable you to travel in a straight line more easily.

10. Do not attempt to walk across an open space unless absolutely necessary. If you have to, under no circumstances look at your feet. Fix your eyes on an object in the middle distance and count each step in your head. Do not stop walking until you have arrived at where you are going.

get Britain...

OOZER

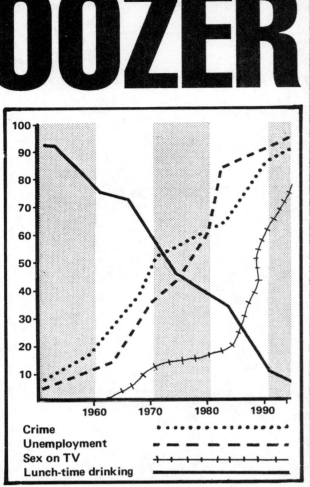

100				
90				
80				
70				
60				
50				
40				
30				
20				
10				
	1960	1970	1980	1990

Crime · · · · · ·
Unemployment – – –
Sex on TV +—+—+—+
Lunch-time drinking ———

The figures (above) speak for themselves.

WE'RE BOOZING FOR BRITAIN

Let's make Britain Great again!

We're launching our own campaign to get Britain back in the boozer and restore traditional values, such as lunch-time drinking. And we want YOU to join in.

Simply pop into your local pub during your lunch break and drink as many pints of beer as you can. Have a sandwich first, to line your stomach, followed by up to twenty pints of beer. Then ask the landlord to sign the form below, and send it to us. In return we'll send you a

splendid Certificate to prove that you helped get Britain back in the boozer, at lunch-time.

Complete this form then send it to: Boozing for Britain, Viz, P.O. Box 1PT, Newcastle upon Tyne NE99 1PT.

I can vouch for the fact that _____

was in my pub at lunch-time on _____ (date) and that

he/she drank _____ pints.

Signed _____ Landlord

Your address _____

Yabba dabba doo

A senior Tory MP is urging for a return to Stone Age values to help solve the problems of rising crime, unemployment and too much sex on TV in Britain today.

Tory wants return to Stone Age values

Sir Anthony Regents-Park, MP for Fulchester Sunny-oak, last night called for a 'back to basics' approach to be adopted in schools, prisons and society as a whole. And he has launched a plan to put Britain back on the rails, with an emphasis on a return to Stone Age values, and children being encouraged to behave in a prehistoric manner.

BLOW

"We need to instil discipline in our children, and what better way to do that than by following in the footsteps of prehistoric man. In cave man days bad behaviour was punished with a heavy blow on the head with a stone club. I think a lot of today's so called youth would think again before committing theft and murder if their parents wielded large clubs and wore animal skins", said Sir Anthony yesterday.

HAND

And the right wing MP had his own idea of how young offenders should be treated once they are caught and convicted. "It's an absolute nonsense sending these thugs and layabouts on holiday at the tax-payers' expense. They should make them live in caves, in just a pair of underpants. And if they get hungry, they should be made to chase after dinosaurs, and throw stones at them. Then we'd see how tough these people are. Let's see if they could kill a dinosaur, then eat it. I bet they couldn't"

PART-TIME

Sir Anthony believes that the solution to our present problems lie in the past. "We can learn from history. Things like the Battle of Hastings, for example, which was in 1066." And he believes that the current decline in family values and the lowering of moral standards can be arrested if we learn from the pages of history.

BANK

"We have become too soft and liberal in our attitudes towards sex. We tend nowadays to refer to women who bring up a family alone as 'single mothers'. What a nonsense. In my day these people were called witches and whores, and, quite rightly, they were burned at the stake. So why not burn them now? Only by getting back to traditional values can we repair the damage that has been done."

SUMMER

Sir Anthony is set to table a motion in the Commons this week asking that prostitutes be ducked in the river Thames from the terrace at Westminster. "If they are witches they will not drown, and we can burn them", he told colleagues.

DESK

Meanwhile, Sir Anthony has insisted that he will not be resigning despite calls from his constituency party for him to quit. The calls came after Sir Anthony stabbed his secretary to death upon discovering she was pregnant with his love child. He then mutilated her naked body, arranging her entrails around her neck. So

Sir Anthony (above) and a Stone Age man yesterday (below)

far no charges have been brought against him.

BOB-A

Denying allegations of murder, Sir Anthony told reporters that the death of his secretary was a personal matter, and did not affect his ability to carry out his job on behalf of his constituents. In 1981 Sir Anthony was forced to resign from his post as Junior Minister at the Home Office after the sex slaying of four prostitutes in the Church-town area of Fulchester, a notorious red light district. Although no charges were brought against him, Sir Anthony's name became linked with the crime when the women's severed heads were found in a freezer at his home.

21

CONFESSIONS OF A MOVIE STAR SHAG-A-LIKE

A Rotherham window cleaner's resemblance to a top movie star is making him a fortune. For lookalike Burt Johnson is charging star-struck women up to £500 for sex.

Dead ringer Burt (right) as Robin, and the discreet ad (below) which he placed in a shop window.

And female fans desperate to fulfil their fantasies have literally been queuing up to pay for sex with Burt since he placed an ad in his local newsagents' window.

GIGOLO

The hunky 54 year old gigolo boosts his paltry £80 a week window cleaning income by charging desperate housewives hundreds of pounds to make their wildest sexual dreams come true. For Burt is a dead ringer for saucy seventies 'Confessions' star Robin Askwith, and for hundreds of sex starved housewives, Burt is as close to the real thing as they will ever get.

FIGARO

Our investigator rang the phone number which was given on the back of Johnson's post card and asked how much it would cost to book the Robin Askwith lookalike for one night. Johnson told her that the price would depend on what exactly she wanted.

ANGELO

"I could do you sex in the back of the car, with the windows steaming up, the bonnet springing open, the suspension bouncing up and down and steam coming out of the radiator, for £500. But doors falling off would be extra," he told her.

ROMEO

"If you don't want to spend that much I do straight sex in a lift for £250. That includes the lift going up and down very very fast and the lift indicator arrow frantically waving backwards and forwards. If you want a group of nuns to be waiting outside for the lift eventually stops that would be another £100."

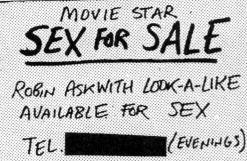

Our investigator arranged to meet Johnson at a local hotel. He strolled in ten minutes late wearing bell bottom jeans, a large floppy cap and a cap sleeved T-shirt several sizes too small. He introduced himself as Robin, and looked down her cleavage before wolf whistling and wiping his brow.

FOXTROT

After being handed an advance payment of £200 cash Johnson agreed to accompany our reporter to a room on the second floor. At first he seemed nervous, but once inside he began to relax a little and said that he had been working as a lookalike escort for about a year. He said he worked for five or six nights a week, usually as Robin Askwith, but he did occasionally do Sid James or Kenneth Williams.

VICTOR

Our reporter then asked him if he would be prepared to do straight sex on the bed. He said he would, and that for £500 he would have sex with her until all the bed springs went 'boing', the legs collapsed, and the bed fell through the floor and into the room below where an old couple would be

The real McCoy - seventies sauce pot Robin Askwith.

watching TV. "If you want the old couple not to notice and keep watching telly as if nothing had happened that would be £25 extra," he said.

TANGO

When offered champagne Johnson suggested that he have sex with our reporter in order to make the cork spontaneously pop out of the bottle, causing champagne to spray all over her buttocks, but she declined.

In a taped conversation Johnson also boasted how in the past he had once had sex in a kitchen causing the kettle to boil, the whistle to blow furiously before popping out and flying across the room, and various cupboards to pop open and the contents, including flour, to scatter all over the place. "The food mixer started getting faster and faster, spraying us with chocolate sauce, and two bits of burnt toast popped out of the toaster at the same time" he said, gesturing with his hands.

CRESTA

He then described how on another occasion he had sex on a snooker table, causing all the balls to fly into the pockets.

PEPSI MAX

Our investigator suggested that she may be interested in something more kinky, and asked Johnson if there was anything 'special' he could recommend. His face cracked into a crude smile as he suggested they have sex backstage at a theatre among the props and costumes. "After a few minutes the backdrop will slowly rise to reveal the audience staring at us in disbelief. But I'll keep going, and after you come the audience will burst into a spontaneous standing ovation, at which point I'll grin and bow." He said that would cost £700, but he'd need a couple of days' notice to sort a theatre out. At this point our reporter made her excuses and left.

26

29

LetterBocks
Viz Commick
P.O. Box 1 PT
Newcastle upon Tyne
NE99 1PT

Fat Bastard

It's great to see Dawn French posing in glossy magazines and telling women that it's okay to be fat and that fat birds should be happy with their bodies. That's all well and good. But I for one wouldn't fancy sticking my nose up her bum crack on a hot day.

T. Cheviot
Chester

I am a specky stamp collector, and I'm particularly interested in New Zealand stamps. I thought you might like to brighten up your Letterbocks page for the benefit of your sexist male readership with this stamp. It was issued in 1958, and shows a Maori bint who was a bit of a Daryl Hannah mermaid type, and as readers can no doubt see, she's got her tits out.

Bobby Brown
Croydon

Do any other specky readers collect stamps? More important, have you got any dirty ones? Come on. We're having a dirty stamp competition, and the sender of the dirtiest one will win all the stamps we receive! Not very many, I'd imagine. But anyway, send the stamps to our Letterbocks address. Sorry, stamps cannot be returned except to the winner.

Solar powered calculators with no 'OFF' buttons are a waster of the sun's energy. If you own one, put it under a hat when not in use.

Don Croy
Surrey

Have any other readers spotted the uncanny resemblance between the late Tory MP, sexual deviant and broadcaster Stephen Milligan and Mr Hugo Guthrie, the Tipton entrepreneur who occasionally appears in Viz. Surely this is worth a fiver?

Rob Dixon & Ian Little
Bath, Avon

Clever Bastard

As an intelligent University Professor, I simply have to complain about the cartoon (issue 64) in which a magnet is used to hoist Jimmy Saville up by his gold jewellery. The intensity of the magnetization of a metal, 'J' (in this case gold), is determined by the magnetic field strength 'H' applied to it, multiplied by the magnetic susceptibility 'k' of the material itself, i.e. J=kH. As gold is a diamagnetic material which has a small negative 'k', it will weakly repel the magnetic field applied to it, whatever the strength of 'H'.

Professor Jason Collier
University of Leigh

What the professor means is that magnets can't pick up gold jewellery.

HA-HA! THE MAGNET HAS LIFTED SAVILE UP BY HIS GOLD JEWELLERY. NOW FOR OUR CONCERT TO RAISE MONEY FOR AIDS!

It's interesting to hear all the feminists wailing and cheering Lorena Bobbit for cutting off her husband's penis. But I bet it would be a different story if some poor battered husband had filled up his wife's crack with Polyfilla.

Will Pearson
Leicester

Do any of your readers know of an effective way of attaching cheese to soap? If anyone has any ideas please could they contact me at the following address.

Bob Watkins, Editor
Cheese and Soap Modeller
P.O. Box 2
Peterborough

Not so clever bastards

Despite being brainy students at Oxford University, we are at a loss to understand what the word 'pagga' means, as featured on your 'Have A Fight' T-shirt. It doesn't seem to appear in the dictionary, or any of the other big books that we have got.

Jules & Matt
Dept. of Materials
Oxford University

Imagine if you lost the boat race, and half a dozen of you went after the Cambridge crew to give them a good kicking. But when you got to their place there was half a dozen of them waiting for you. A pagga would ensue.

These new 'Ultra Pampers' nappies are shite. On the TV ad they can hold 4 pints of funny blue liquid. I tried them on my kids, unfortunately none of whom piss windscreen washer fluid, and at the slightest trace of urine there was piss puddles all over the floor. As for turds, you'd have more chance of catching them crawling round behind your baby with a tea strainer in your hand.

J. Bendix
Leicester

If the people who make Fairy Liquid simply diluted the stuff they wouldn't have to spend all that money on TV adverts telling people how strong it is.

Y. Bell
Norfolk

Theiving bastards

If any of the bastards who keep trying to break into my garage are reading this, there's fuck all in there worth nicking.

S. A. Franks
Banbury, Oxon

The other day I noticed I had a flat tyre on my car so I asked the man at the garage to blow it up for me. Imagine my surprise when the car exploded seconds later. Then I realised why. The mechanic was a member of an active IRA terrorist cell, and I am his commanding officer. Do I win £5?

P. McGinty
Co. Armagh

Tourists hoping to buy an ice cream in Britain this summer are going to be confused by the bright yellow 'Cone Hotline' signs which are appearing at motorway roadworks up and down the country. Perhaps another sign with a picture of an ice cream and an arrow could be placed nearby, directing motorists to the nearest ice cream van.

D. Saville
Wimbledon

'Money can't buy me love'. So sang Lennon and McCartney in the sixties. But I can't help thinking that perhaps they could have avoided ending up hitched to a couple of boilers like Yoko and Linda if they'd spent a bit of their cash on decent haircuts, instead of both using the same pudding bowl.

T. Robin Gristle
Bristol

It's no wonder that so many people are catching AIDS nowadays. Houses are full of germs, due to double glazing and central heating. Very few people bother opening their windows to let fresh air in any more.

Mrs B. Nevis
Airdrie

I couldn't disagree more with Mrs. Nevis (Letterbocks, this page) when she says that AIDS is due to double glazing. My husband and I spent £8,000 having our house double glazed in 1981, and I am pleased to report that neither us nor our children have got AIDS. Surely it is the case that sealed windows keep these germs out, rather than in.

Mrs M. Snowdon
Cardiff

Having just read your pathetically childish 'Kipper Quiz' (this issue, page 46), I thought you might be interested in this street name I spotted recently in the Gateshead area.

A. Hill
Felling, Tyne & Wear

I thought this number plate which I spotted in Germany was pretty funny, but having just seen A. Hill's street name (above) my photo looks rather dull by comparison. Still, I don't suppose it's worth a fiver, is it?

Big Al Ross
St. Albans

Fuck off, bastard

Was issue 64 some sort of warped marketing experiment? I refer not to the pink and yellow 'Blobby' cover, but to the crud behind it. Whilst the decline of Viz has been well documented and is widely accepted, issue 64 set an unprecedented low point. Was the idea to measure the effects of a particularly poor issue on subsequent sales? I for one will not be reading Viz again.

Peter Phelan
Monkstown, Co. Dublin

Hey. If we could think of a better way of making a living we would. Meanwhile, it's thanks to miserable cunts like you that we have to keep putting the price up.

Further to all the letters in previous issues, if you students are so good at getting 'proper jobs', why are you always working as waiters, door-to-door salesmen and strippers?

W. Neast
Twining

P.S. And prostitutes.

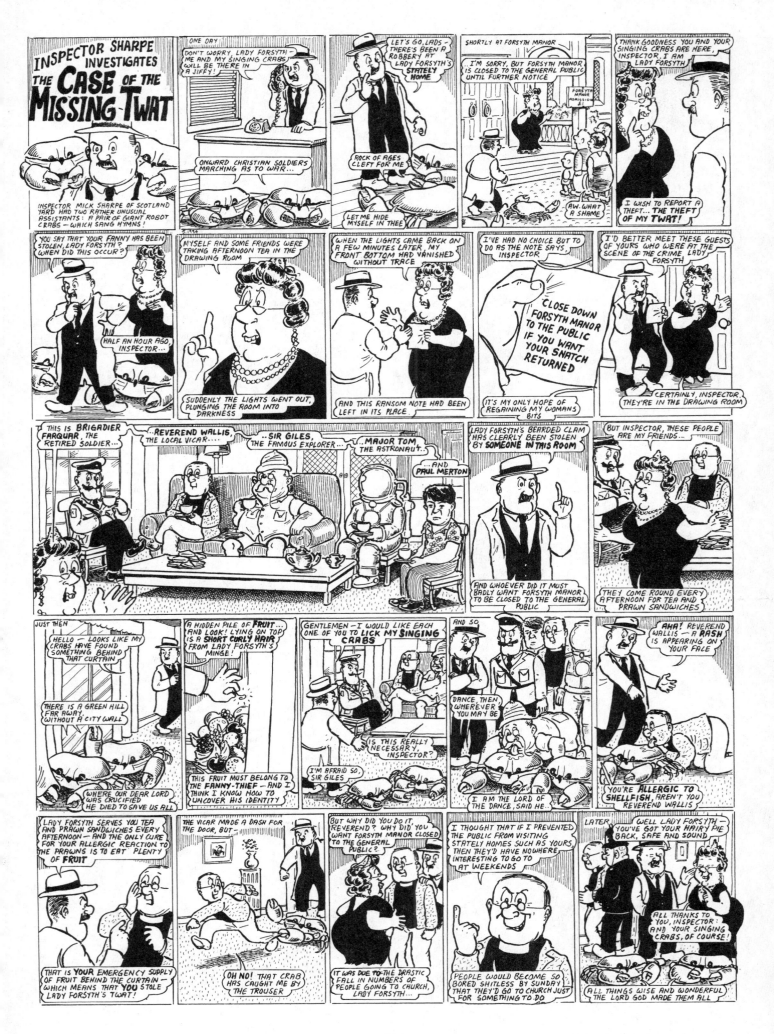

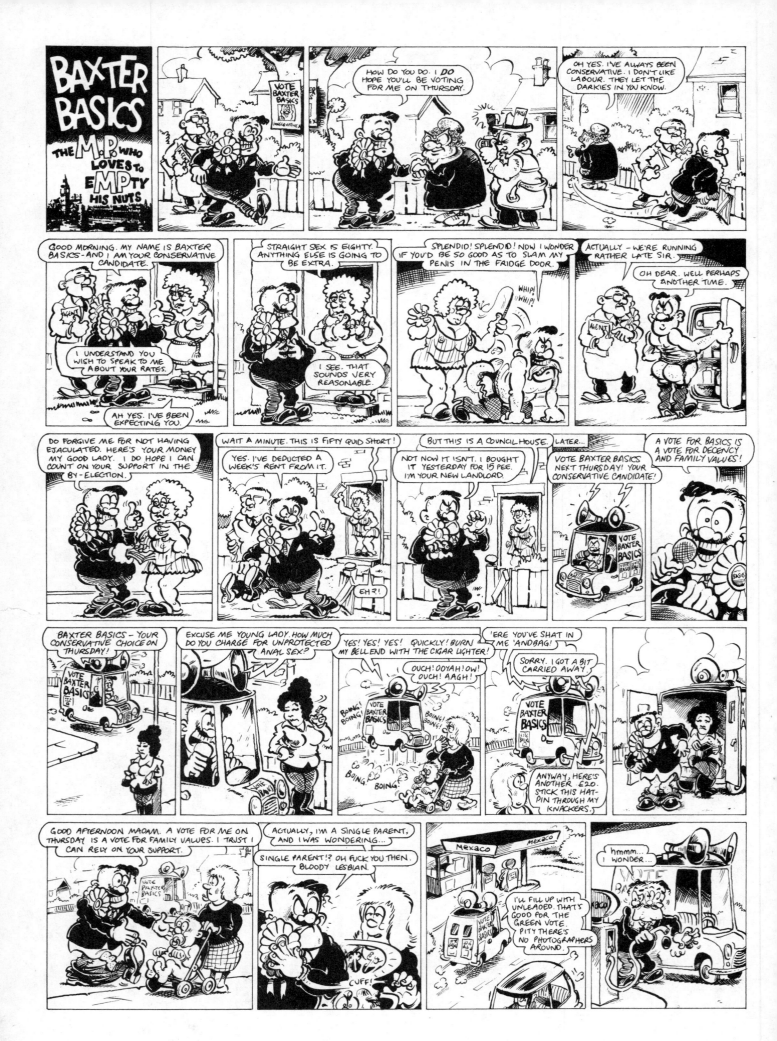

TOP TIPS

★★★ ●■●■●■● ★★★★ ●■●■●■● ★★★

DON'T fork out for expensive smoke alarms. Simply fill balloons with water and hang them from the ceiling. Then cover the floor with air-filled balloons, each with a drawing pin stuck to the top. If a fire starts, the hot air will cause the balloons to rise up from the floor and burst the balloons with water in, thus extinguishing the fire. Probably.

D. P.
Wiltshire

TRANSFORM your garden into a 'EuroDisney' style theme park by charging your neighbour £20 to get in, £5 for an ice cream, and then making him wait 4 hours for a ride on your lawn mower.

S. Tempest
Plymouth

MARRIED COUPLES. Find out where you live in relation to other buildings in your neighbourhood by driving to a nearby hill while your 'other half' lets off an emergency flare from the bedroom window.

R. Worsnop
Chesterfield

LIE Jacobs cream crackers on a 'mattress' consisting of two slices of processed cheese wrapped in kitchen paper, before buttering. This will help distribute pressure evenly across the back of the biscuit, and prevent cracking.

H. Lloyd
Runcorn

NON-SWIMMERS. Fill a pair of goggles with water and put them on. You'll then experience all the pleasures of swimming without getting wet or having to travel to your nearest pool.

Andrew Powell
Portsmouth

FEEL like a million dollars next time you arrive home by gluing Rice Krispies onto your car tyres. When you park it will sound just like an expensive gravel drive.

D. Treloar
Wandsworth

A BLACK bin liner draped over an old TV aerial makes a cheap yet effective umbrella, particularly handy in these wet and blustery spring months.

D. Topper
Woking

SAVE the cost of installing cable TV by taping current editions of Top Of The Pops and then watch them in fifteen years time.

Lex Mouzer
Liverpool

OBTAIN the effect of New Year's Eve revelling without the expense this year by staying in and watching TV. Then wash your teeth in turpentine, drink a glass of washing-up liquid, and hit your head on the wall a few times before going to bed.

W. Fascia
Kettering

VICARS. Raise much needed restoration funds by inviting the owners of lost pets to climb to the top of your steeple in order to look for their missing animals, in return for a small donation.

B. O. Nails
Nantwich

APPLY red varnish to your fingernails before clipping them. The red clippings will be much easier to spot on your carpet. (Unless you have a red carpet, in which case a contrasting nail varnish should be selected.)

K. Parks
North Chittagong

BETTER still, why not paint them with gold nail varnish, and then pick them up easily and quickly using a magnet.

Professor Jason Collier
Leigh University

GIRLS. Next time you feel like throwing a ball overarm, don't do it, because you can't and it looks very silly. Just throw it girlie underarm style and no-one will laugh at you or get hurt.

D. Thresher
Wapping

CALCULATE the exact time of a bus journey by strapping a watch to a rail or handle on the bus, and noting the time of departure. By meeting the bus on its return and checking the watch, you will have the precise journey time.

M. Greenwood
Goole

NEXT time you fill your tyres with air at the garage charge the attendant 10p for each breath you take while you're talking to him.

D. Thompson
Wivenhoe

The MAN in the PUB

Britain's most ill-informed columnist

Did you know that Lester Piggott fella is SIX foot tall. Wouldn't think it to look at him on the telly, would you? But he is. Six foot.

You think about it. How many times have you seen his legs? Always riding a horse, isn't he. Keeps 'em bent all the time, you see.

You know that Cilla Black. She makes all her own clothes. No... she DOES. And that's true that is. Makes them out of curtains, you know. Wouldn't think it to look at her on the telly. Does a marvellous job.

Makes her own shoes as well, apparently.

I'll tell you who's got money. That Dennis Waterman. He was the original Milky Bar Kid you know. Imagine him... the bloke out of Minder ... with glasses. It's him, isn't it. Got paid a fortune for them ads, I reckon.

You know that racing commentator, Murray whatsisname. He invented the slogan 'GO TO WORK ON AN EGG'. He did, I'm telling you. Used to work in advertising. So did my Aunt Marie. She invented Bovril. And you know Baileys Irish Cream. A mate of mine's Uncle, he invented that. Made a fortune.

Did you know you can cut glass with a pair of scissors, if you do it UNDERWATER. That's true. A mate of mine did it.

Our Teacher's a Wardrobe

QUICK, EVERYBODY! HE'S COMING!

CHOP! THERE GO COCK AGA

John Thomas Choppit is a bonking miracle. For he has lost count of the number of times his penis has been severed. And while America makes a meal out of a man whose member has gone missing only once, here is the story of a brave Brit whose manhood has been cut off more times than a person who habitually fails to pay their telephone bill (and then subsequently pays the reconnection charge). Here, John tells his own amazing story

The true story of John Thomas Choppit's chopped John Thomas

' Everyone got pretty excited when they heard about the American guy whose wife chopped off his manhood. But I didn't. The truth is that I've had my cock chopped off more times than he's had hot dinners. Yet somehow or other I've always managed to get it back again.

PROBLEM

Finding it has never been a problem for me. Because in my case there's rather a lot to look for, if you know what I mean. You could say it *sticks out a bit*. So if my wife chucked it into a hedge – which she has done once or twice – it would be pretty easy to spot.

LETTERS

But my wife is by no means the only person who has cut my cock off. Funnily enough, it's usually a completely innocent accident. Like the time I was working in a butcher's shop when a good looking bird came in to buy a bit of pork. Little did she know she'd soon be walking out of the shop with *my* pork sausage in her shopping bag!

ELAINE

I was feeling pretty horny as I looked this bird up and down and my old man quickly sprang into action. Most people can manage to conceal it, but in my case it's like trying to hide a telegraph pole in a paper bag. The bird obviously liked what she saw, 'cos she started to lick her lips. That must have distracted me, cost at that moment instead of chopping her chop, I brought down my chopper and chopped straight through my pride and joy!

At first I didn't realise what I'd done. I just wrapped it in brown paper, weighed it and handed it to her. It was a bit more than she'd asked for, so I gave her a couple of bob off. She winked, and left the shop. It wasn't until she got home and started frying it that she realised there'd been a cock up. Or *cock off* to be more precise.

JIMMY

Meanwhile, the coin dropped and I realised something was amiss. Little did I know my knob had become Britain's first *frying* pan handle as it simmered in an Uncle Ben barbecue sauce two miles away. I was just starting to panic when the bird came running back into the shop waving my old fella in her hand. It was quite a relief to see it again, I can tell you. Luckily, this bird was a nurse, so we went in the back of the shop and she stitched it back on for me straight away.

SPORTS

It felt a bit hot, but that was probably due to the spicy sauce she'd been frying it in. "I'll lick the sauce off for you if you like", she said. I didn't need asking twice!

FALL

If I'd had any doubts about my manhood working again (which I hadn't), I needn't have. 'Cos I'll tell you what. That bird might not have got the pork chop she was after, but she ended up with one hell of a *mouthful of meat!* In fact, she reckoned it was the best bit of *sweet and sour pork* she's ever had! And I reckoned it was a pretty good blow job and all.

WHEEL

Unfortunately, there isn't always a sexy nurse on hand to stick my cock back on. So usually it's a case of picking it up, chucking it in a bag, and heading off to the local hospital. Providing it's still in one piece!

WINGS

I'll never forget the time I had a mishap with my lawn mower. With an electric mower there's always a danger of cutting through the

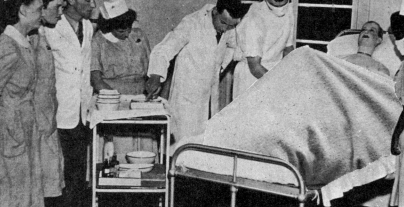

All in a day's work. Staff at the local hospital stand by as surgeons begin the delicate task of sewing John Thomas Choppit's cock on. Again.

flex. But little did I know I was about to cut through my own *flex* – and there was nothing electric about the shock I got!

PRESSURE

It was a hot sunny day, so I'd decided to strip off, in the privacy of my own back garden. But unfortunately, being as well endowed as I am, my cock tends to trail along behind me, which makes mowing the lawn a bit awkward. As I cut the grass, moving backwards and forwards, I began to get it in a bit of a tangle. Next thing I knew I'd actually mowed through my manhood.

BOARD

There was cock all over the place. A top chef couldn't have sliced it finer. But I managed to get all the bits together and headed off down the street towards the hospital. I felt a proper idiot, walking along bollock naked carrying my cock in a carrier bag. But I was in luck, as round the corner I bumped into an ice cream van.

I knew that it would help the doctors if my cock was packed in ice, but the ice cream man said he didn't have any. So I bought about a dozen ice lollies instead, and chucked them into the bag. By the time I got to the hospital most of them had melted, but it had been cold enough to keep my willie in A1 condition, and the doctors managed to stick it back on while I waited.

CARD

For a few days after that my girlfriend kept giving me blow jobs every twenty minutes and telling me it was 'Fab'. I didn't know why until I looked down and noticed the tip of my knob was chocolate coated and covered in hundreds and thousands!

PARTY

To be quite honest I've lost count of the number of times I've had my willie chopped off. The police usually recognise my knob if they find it lying around and either bring it to my house or take it straight to the hospital. But finding it can

sometimes be a problem, like the time when I was working on a farm.

COMPUTER

It was summer, so I was cutting the grass with a combine harvester. After a while there was a bump and the machine stopped. I'd run over a cow, and it had got stuck in the threshers. I climbed in to try and rescue it, but I forgot to put the handbrake on, and next thing you know the cow jumped out and the machine started up, dragging me into the blades.

BALL

Next thing I knew I awoke inside a haystack. My arm was sore, and my cock felt numb. I later realised they had both been chopped off. Anyway, I climbed out and found my arm more or less straight away. But there was no sign of my willie. Looking for a cock in a haystack with only one hand is not the easiest of tasks, I can tell you. After a few hours it got dark, so I gave up and went home, stopping at the local hospital to have

32

ES MY IN

my arm sewed back on. That night as I lay in bed without a cock I felt so depressed I just wanted to die. It was as if I was no longer a real man.

STOP

The next morning I got up and decided to have Weetabix for breakfast. And I could hardly believe what happened next. For when I opened the packet there it was – staring out at me. My cock! Stuck in a Weetabix. The haystack must have been taken to the factory and made into Weetabix, with my cock still in it. Fortunately it hadn't been damaged and I had it sewn back on later that morning.

BIG

Having your own penis fall out of a cereal packet in front of you is a lot more exciting that finding a plastic dinosaur, I can tell you. But the thought of it has put me oft Weetabix for good. I think I'll try Crunchy Nut Corkflakes in future, and just hope that my bollocks never get chopped off (if you know what I mean!).

SOFT

Funnily enough, losing my cock on numerous occasions has never affected my love life. Most girls find it quite exciting when it comes off, and they like to hold it on the way to the hospital. But my first visit to hospital was difficult. Lying there in the ward, without a cock, I felt like I was no longer a real man. I was sure the nurses would laugh at me. But when the doctor ordered a dozen rolls of thread just to sew it back on, they began to pay attention! In fact, it took him four hours to sew all the way around it, and that was using a sewing machine! By the time he'd finished there was a queue of nurses a mile long all waiting to give me a bed bath.

There have been other funny moments too. Like the time I had a mountaineering accident, and ended up trapped by my cock half way up Mount Everest. A huge boulder had landed on it, and I couldn't move. The only answer was to cut it off, otherwise I'd have been stuck there forever.

HARD

Cutting your own cock off half way up Mount Everest is no fun, I can tell you. It hurt so much I let out a scream. That was a bad mistake, because next thing I knew there was an avalanche, and me and my cock were both buried under tons of snow. Little did I know that frozen in the ice right below me was the remains of a dinosaur, perfectly preserved for thousands of years.

CHEESEY

When they rescued me, instead of finding my cock, they accidentally picked up the dinosaur's, because they were both about the same size. Anyway, they stitched it back on, and off I went home. It wasn't until a few days later that I realised something was wrong.

DINOSAUR'S

I'd gone to see the film 'Jurassic Park' when I suddenly started to fancy lady dinosaurs. I mentioned it to my doctor and he decided to take a urine sample. The following week he rang me up to say that the results were positive – my sample had turned out to be *dinosaur piss*. At first he was baffled, but I soon explained the mix-up.

JIG

Three weeks later a rescue helicopter spotted my real cock. They only just managed to winch it on board. Luckily the snow and ice had preserved it and the doctor was able to swap it for my dinosaur cock quite easily. My wife was sad to see the dinosaur cock go, as she'd enjoyed Tyranosaurus sex sessions with me and my *prehistoric bone on*. But goodness only knows what might have happened if she'd become pregnant. **9**

Trevor's book, 'How My Cock Keeps Getting Chopped Off', is published by Sea Lion Books, priced £18.99.

McCLOUD CUCKOO LAND

A bitter feud has divided the Norfolk town of Cromer over a planning application for a multi million dollar theme park.

Opponents of the plan have raised strong objections to local planning chiefs after it was revealed that a 6,000 acre site in the middle of the town would be bulldozed, leaving hundreds of residents homeless, and affecting scores of local businesses.

PARK

The ambitious planning application for a 'Disney' style theme park to replace the existing Cromer town centre has been filed by former American TV cop Dennis Weaver. Weaver, who played 'urban cowboy' Marshall Sam McCloud in the hit series has been finalising details of his 'McCloud' based theme park for several months, and if permission is granted he hopes to have it open by Spring 1995.

GRID

If the controversial scheme is given the green light 'McCloud Cuckoo Land' will become Britain's biggest theme park, incorporating roundabouts with horses on them, cowboy style target ranges, a roller coaster, a dolphinarium, coconut shies, crazy golf (with a windmill) and hot dog stands, all based on the eccentric cowboy cop whose catchphrase was "Now there you go", said slowly, in a cowboy voice.

HUNT

But a campaign of opposition to the scheme is gathering momentum. And Cromer's most celebrated residents, The Partridge Family, have joined in with the swell of public opinion against the development. Partridge Family spokesman David Cassidy said that Weaver's scheme would spell disaster for Cromer.

HILL

"We moved here in the late seventies, shortly after our hits, which included 'I think I love you', dried up", he told a local newspaper yesterday. "We were particularly attracted to the pretty town centre, with its flint buildings. To demolish those buildings would be madness, and would spell disaster for the community of Cromer. The Partridge Family are not prepared to stand by and watch the beautiful heart being ripped out of this pleasant Norfolk coastal town", he added.

Dennis Weaver as TV's McCloud (above) and TV's Partridge Family (right) with David Cassidy (fifth from dog, clockwise).

However Weaver, smelling slightly of piss and speaking from his home in the middle of a pile of car tyres in nearby Sheringham, was quick to counter Cassidy's claims. And he insisted that McLoud Cuckoo Land would be a boost for tourism in the area. "I am prepared to invest millions of dollars which I have earned playing TV cop McCloud in the seventies, and more recently endorsing revolutionary car care products on the shopping channel, in Cromer. And I hope the planning authority will have the vision to back this scheme"

CAMPBELL

He also blasted The Partridge Family, accusing the former seventies singing TV family of sour grapes. "It is common knowledge in Norfolk that The Partridge Family recently had a similar application, for a theme park to be called 'Partridge Family In A Pear Tree Land', turned down by Lowestoft planning committee".

DEAN

Weaver's application will be considered by the council's planning sub committee next Tuesday. Two years ago he failed to win approval for an ambitious development which he had planned to launch into space. 'McLoud Base Nine' was to have been the world's first orbiting space theme park, but came within the jurisdiction of Cromer's planning authority as it was to have been launched from a car park adjacent to the town's railway station.

34

LetterBocks

That's magic!

They say 'you can't teach an old dog new tricks'. Well Paul Daniels hasn't done too badly with Debbie McGee.

Mr C. Pops
Halifax

*LetterBocks
Viz Commick
P.O. Box 1 PT
Newcastle upon Tyne
NE99 1PT*

My brother-in-law is Cockney Wanker's double. He's from the East End, supports West Ham, and he even eats jellied eels. Here's a picture of him. Do I win £100?

John Warham
Kowloon

* A pretty good likeness, and well worth a hundred pounds. But before we send you the money, does anyone else know a Viz look-a-like? If you send us a picture of a more impressive look-a-like than John's, YOU can have John's £100. And there'll be a tenner... no, we'll make it £20 for any other pictures we decide to print. If you want them returned, put your name and address on the back.

I wonder if any of your readers could help me. I am looking for a great big melting pot sufficiently large to accommodate the world and all it's got. If I find one my intention is to keep it stirring for a hundred years or possibly longer, my eventual aim being to turn out coffee coloured people in multiples of twenty. Is anyone aware of a manufacturer or supplier of melting pots large enough for this purpose?

B. Mink
Birmingham

On a recent trip to Spain I spotted this car. Is nobody safe from the Bottom Inspectors?

Dave Richardson
Madrid

P.S. Do I win £5?

*Yes Dave, there's a crisp fiver on its way to you.

My husband and I couldn't believe all the fuss over the D-Day anniversary. We have been quietly commemorating the event every June for the last forty years. During our annual holiday in Great Yarmouth my husband puts on a rucksack filled with housebricks and wades about in the sea for several hours while I shoot at him with an air rifle from the promenade. It's our own personal way of paying tribute to the bravery and the sacrifices made by those who took part.

Mrs R. Split
Fareham

Have any other readers spotted a car or sign or anything else with the word 'ARSE' written on it? Send you photos to 'Arse Snaps' at our usual Letterbocks address. There's between £5 and £20 for each picture we use, depending how big the word 'ARSE' is.

Having witnessed your recent decline in standards I thought perhaps now would be a good time to write in and tell you that I live in a village called 'Cocking'. I would love to hear from readers who live in a foreign village called 'Fanny' or similar so that we could arrange for the two places to be twinned.

B. J.
Cocking (Nr. Midhurst)
West Sussex

Star bore

I was disappointed to find a glaring inaccuracy in your cartoon 'Derek Anorak' (issue 65). Any true 'anorak' would know there were 124 episodes of Star Trek made, not 513 as claimed in your strip. This excludes the original pilot episode in which Captain Kirk was absent, a Captain Decker being in command. Captain Decker later reappeared in episode 56, severely disabled and in an electric wheelchair.

Kevin Davies
Wisbech, Cambs.

* The many thousands of girls who'd no doubt like to go out with a bright, observant Star Trek fan called Kevin can write c/o our Letterbocks address and we'll forward your letters to him.

What a surprise. That bearded twat Richard Branson buys a stake in Viz and suddenly it's full of shitty 'jokes' about Radio One. Well you can tell him from me that Radio One is still infinitely better than the bollocks he turns out on that old folk's home he calls a radio station. And you can shove your magazine up your arse from now on.

Ian Bryson
Preston

* Yeah? Well you can shove your radio up your arse an' all, you big Lancashire ponce.

In reply to Bob Watkins' letter (issue 65). One way of attaching cheese to soap could be to pin them by sticking a sewing needle into the soap and then sliding the cheese onto it and pushing them firmly together. I cannot guarantee success, but it has always worked for me when attaching potatoes to cucumbers.

C. Ooffack, Deputy Editor
Potato & Cucumber
Modeller

Big isn't beautiful

If Dawn French thinks fat people are so beautiful, how come she didn't marry Barry White?

G. Nuggets
Welwyn

I am writing in reply to the gentleman from Cocking (Letterbocks, this issue). I believe the town of Muff, in County Donegal, would be ideally suited for twinning with his village. I don't live there, but could you send me £5 anyway?

Peter Groarke
Rathfarnham, Dublin

Here's my entry for your Dirty Stamp competition (issue 65). Something for your sexist female readers, rather than the blokes. It's a Russian stamp, and if you look closely it shows a bunch of naked men riding round on horses, in a pond.

Yvonne Muller
Zurich

Rude stamps? Try these for size. They make your New Zealand one look tame. These are from Equatorial Guinea. God knows where that is, but they do a pretty hot line in filthy postage stamps.

Jeremy Harris
Cheltenham

* Congratulations Jeremy. You win all the other stamps we received. Four altogether. We'll also chuck in a free subscription, and a can of lager. Plus a copy of the Fat Slags new book, sixty dollars in American money, and a tape measure.

She's no angel

People are quick to criticise Michael Aspel for his extra-marital romps, and a lot of sympathy has been expressed for his wife. What short memories some people have. It was only a few months ago that Aspel's wife, Mrs Hewitt, was shagging Arthur Fowler in EastEnders. Frankly, I think the pair of them deserve each other.

Mrs R. Brek
Northampton

When oh when are people going to shut up about Charles Dickens? The man's been dead for over 100 years. It's about time people showed a little sympathy for his family, and stopped talking about him all the time on the television and the radio.

Mrs S. Wheat
Grangemouth

Woman, 66, hit by snatch thief

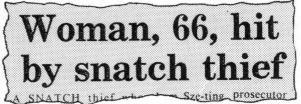

A SNATCH thief ... Sze-ting, prosecutor

After reading Inspector Sharpe and the case of the Missing Twat (issue 65) I thought the officer concerned may like to look into this interesting case which came up recently in Hong Kong, as reported by the South China Post. Do I win HKD 115.59?

R.J.P.
Mid Levels, Hong Kong

On a recent holiday in Spain my husband and I were offered a bunch of peculiar sausage shaped fruits, the yellow skins of which peeled off in 'flaps' to reveal a creamy coloured flesh inside. They were delicious, and I have since discovered that these are called 'bananas'. Do any readers know whether they are available in Britain, and if so where they can be purchased?

Mrs W. Abix
Arbroath

With all the recent tragedies that have occurred in the world of Formula One motor racing it seems a pity that Nigel Mansell is no longer involved in the sport.

Mr S. H. Reddies
Doncaster

In the last issue we anticipated a series of Grand Prix motor racing tragedies and asked for your suggestions to make Formula One racing safer. The following are just a few of your replies.

I think traffic calming measures like 'sleeping policemen' should be installed on motor racing circuits. These are being used in busy streets all over Britain and the result has been slower cars and fewer accidents.

Mrs S. F. Brains
Winchester

Cardboard cut outs of police cars positioned on bridges overlooking the track would soon slow drivers down.

Mr O. Crunchies
Aberdeen

How about a picture of former BBC newsreader Richard Baker wearing a chunky jumper and drinking beer?

Mrs A. Bran
Derby

Only too happy to oblige Mrs Bran.

Do any other readers have unusual picture requests? We'd love to hear from you, no matter how strange your request is. And if we can't find the picture you're after, we'll send you £100! How about that for a challenge?

Formula for disaster

Formula One race organisers should follow the example set by Scalextric and have unmanned racing cars driven along grooves in the track by remote control. If the drivers felt that watching from a safe distance lacked excitement, they could be strapped into a chair and race officials could hit them with a cricket bat every time their car crashed.

Mr Q. Oats
Kilmarnock

Bewes sets target for walnut industry

Former TV Likely Lad Rodney Bewes has set a target for Britain's walnut growing industry. 'Self sufficiency by the year 1997.'

Bewes believes that Britain should be growing all the nuts we need within three years, and that the target is realistic. "I don't know much about walnuts, or how you grow them, but I think that we should be producing as many as we need, and hopefully within the next three years."

Bewes chose his target - the 6th of February 1997 - mainly because it was the anniversary of a friend's wedding. "I had a gut feeling about 1997, but I must confess a friend of mine suggested the 6th February because it was his wedding anniversary, But I don't suppose that's important."

Bewes, who lives in Putney, South London, played Bob in the popular series. And we asked him how his hen pecking wife Thelma might have reacted to his target walnut self-sufficiency. "I hadn't really thought about that", he confessed. "I seem to remember she was always trying to stop me going to the pub with Terry, my best mate. I don't know. Perhaps she'd think it was a good idea. I'm not sure."

And Bewes was equally uncertain about how Britain's nut growers are supposed to go about increasing their crops. "I suppose if they invested in new technology - some sort of nut fertiliser, or mechanical nut pickers, that would help."

TOP TIPS

MOTORISTS. Remove your trousers and tie them around your neck before getting into your car. You will then be able to remove your handkerchief, keys or wallet from your trouser pocket with ease, even after you have fastened your seat belt.

J. Varley
London N18

VIDEO your goldfish swimming in its bowl, then place a TV set next to the bowl, and play back the tape. Hey presto! Instant 'company' for your fish. Duplicate the tape and use extra televisions to create a 'goldfish party' on special occasions.

Mr B. Lane
Aston Clinton, Bucks.

FELLAS. Next time you have to wrap up a present, don't, because you're shite at it. Give it to the wife and she'll do it properly with extra girlie bows and fiddly bits while you're down the pub.

D. Treloar
Cardiff

INTERNATIONAL master criminals. Tell your guards to shoot James Bond in the head at the first available opportunity. Under no circumstances give him a guided tour of your secret base, or leave him in the custody of women wearing bikinis.

S. Stars
Welwyn

AN EVEN sprinkling of flour will lighten the colour of your carpet. If you don't like the new shade, simply vacuum it off.

C. Jones
Reading

ASK your butcher to thinly slice those old wellington boots, and hey presto! An endless supply of windscreen wiper blades.

D. M.
Farnborough

AMERICAN organised crime leaders. On capturing the 'A' Team do NOT lock them in a shed full of tools and useful scrap materials.

Chris Jones
Reading

POLICEMEN. Walk up and down the street remarking to each other on how the public are getting older every day.

D. Tucker
Chelmslow

INVITE the Gloucester Constabulary to a party. Tell them you'll bring the beer if they can dig up some women.

D. Trotter
Carlisle

A SWISH curtain rail, a pyjama cord and a hat pin provide a cheap but effective bow and arrow for those games of Robin Hood in the park. Alternatively, in these safety conscious times, why not substitute a sink plunger for the hat pin?

Mrs D. Treliss
Colwyn Bay

ARCH villains of Gotham City. Kill Batman and Robin using traditional techniques (gun, knife etc.) rather than leaving them unattended at the mercy of an untested 'Heath Robinson' style killing machine of your own design.

C. Gordon
Gotham City P.D.

REMOVE the laces from odd boots and shoes which you find washed up on the beach. Pop them inside a sock next time you wash any clothes, then dry them with an iron and keep them in an old yogurt carton for use as spares.

A. Houndog
Cumbria

CONVERT black labrador dogs into seals by feeding them pastries, sweets and cakes, starving them of exercise, slipping a pair of black socks onto their front paws, smearing their coats in vaseline and then encouraging them to balance a beach ball on the nose in return for fish shaped dog biscuits.

R. Crosbie
Cheltenham

ENSURE that your copy of Viz arrives on your doormat exactly one week after all your mates have bought theirs in the local newsagents by forking out £7.50 of your hard earned cash for a subscription.

Mr J. Crosby
Shrewsbury

NAIL old floorboards to your trees in order to attract woodpeckers.

Robin Pearce
Southampton

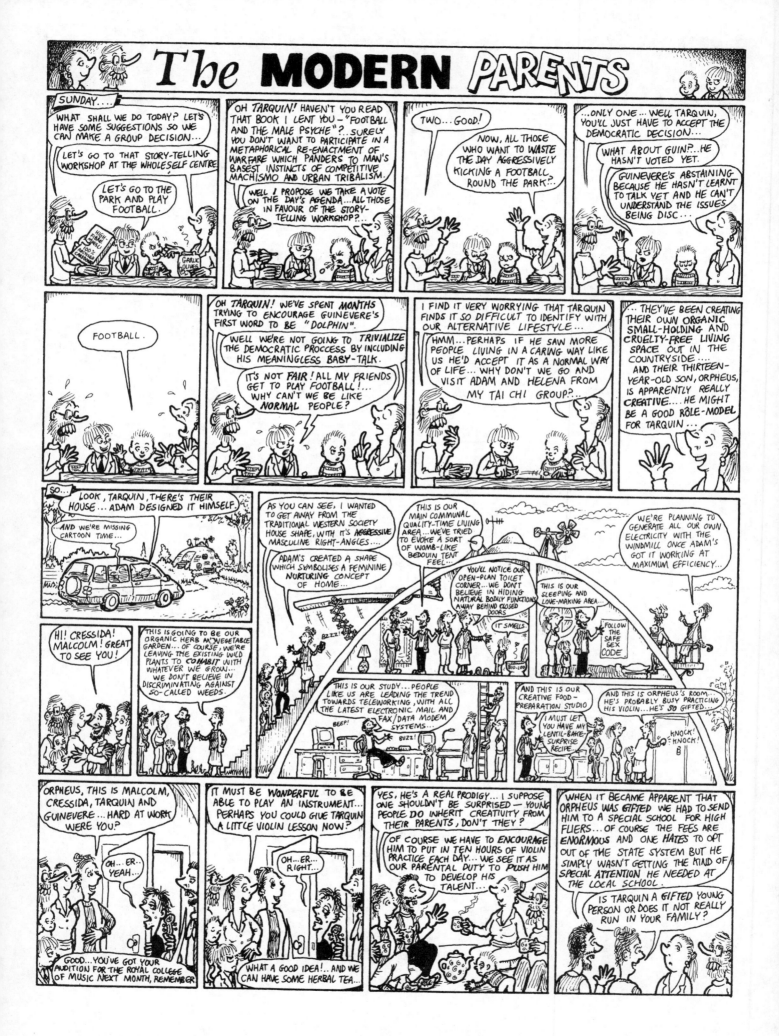

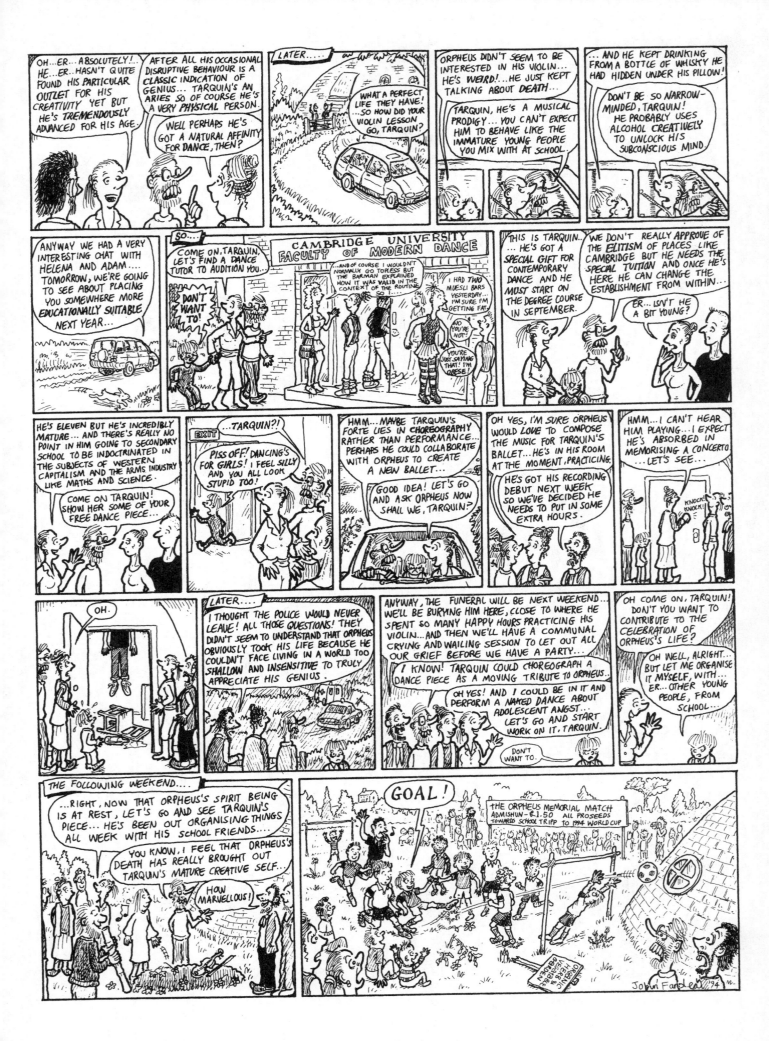

45

47

48

49

PULLING THE BIRDS IS A

Getting that girl is 'easy PC' if you're a New Man

A few years back all you had to do to impress a girl was buy her a drink or a box of chocolates. And wham bam thank you man you were in her knickers.

In the sixties, for example, soccer star George Best only had to stagger into a nightclub and punch someone in the face and hey presto! Half a dozen Miss World's were queuing up for a shag.

MIRROR

But times have changed and the sexist approach no longer does the trick. Nowadays birds are on the lookout for a 'New Man'. Someone who doesn't slap their arse, and stays at home to wash dishes on a Saturday afternoon.

SIGNAL

Ben Elton, for example, doesn't need to drink ten pints of lager and fit a Colonel Bogie horn to his Ford Capri to pick up the skirt. Instead he makes out they're his equal, ridicules sexism and tells jokes about periods. Richard Gere hit the jackpot too,

Bloke Best (above) bird Cindy (below).

Good Gere - Richard's pulled some top notch totty.

pulling sexy supermodel Cindy Crawford by being a Budhist and using chat up lines about the political situation in Tibet.

MANOUVRE

Have you got what it takes to be a New Man? Test yourself by completing this questionnaire. Answer each question a, b or c then tottie up your total and see how you've scored with the liberated women of today.

1. You're in a high brow book shop looking through a thick book with no pictures in it when you spot a classy bit of fluff with her hands full struggling to open the door. What would you do?

Bingo Ben gets his bird proving that 'PC' pays.

(a) Hold the door open, look down her blouse, grin, and slap her on the arse as she leaves.
(b) Hold the door open and smile nervously, trying not to look down at her bust.
(c) Let her open the door herself while you look at the book she's carrying, then tell her how much you admire the author and prattle on about some other books what they've written, until she invites you for a cup of tea.

2. You're walking through the park when you see two gorgeous birds sitting on a bench. Nearby some kids are playing football and their ball lands at your feet. What would you do?

(a) Dribble the ball past the eight year old kids before unleashing a 25 yard shot that sails between the two coats that are being used as goal posts, then run towards the women, your hand raised in the air, shouting "Yeee-es!!!"
(b) Pick the ball up and walk towards the kids, then kick it to them playfully once you're close enough not to risk missing or falling over in the process.
(c) Give them their ball back but tell them, in a loud voice so that the women can hear, you don't approve of the concept of competitive male dominated sports.

3. Your girlfriend says she's hungry and fancies a meal. Where do you go?

(a) To the nearest American style fast food restaurant for a fiver's worth of mad cow, reconstituted chips and a two gallon paper cup of coke.
(b) To a classy Chinese restaurant where you can relax and keep her entertained by making 'flied lice' jokes and playing with your chop sticks.
(c) Back to your place where you can show her how domesticated you are by cooking a five course meal without any chips, and then offering to help with the dishes.

4. You're spending a cosy night in with a date. You've got plenty of booze and the pizzas are on their way. What would you watch on the telly?

(a) Live football on Sky, followed by the highlights on BBC1. The flip over to the Adult Channel at midnight for 15 minutes of free porn.
(b) Flick around to see if there's any good movies on.
(c) Watch 'Newsnight' on BBC2 then sit through the 'The Late Show' pretending to know what the fuck all those pretentious tarts are prattling on about.

5. One evening it gets to 8 o'clock and your missus still hasn't come home from work. How would you react?

(a) Drink half a bottle of whisky then pace up and down convincing yourself she's having an affair with her boss. Then raise the roof when she gets home without giving her a chance to explain where she's been.
(b) Wait till she gets home then demand an explanation. Listen suspiciously to what she has to say, asking occasional trick questions in order to expose any inconsistency in her story.
(c) Say absolutely nothing when she gets home. She's an individual, and its none of your business where she's been. If she wants to have an 'open' relationship that's fine. So hey! There's no need to lay this jealousy trip on her. I mean... after all, it's her body. You don't own her. And don't forget, that means you'll be able to go out and shag other birds as well.

6. You're after a new motor to impress the tooty. What sort of car would you buy?

(a) An old transit van with flames painted on the side, outsized back wheels, disco speakers and an old mattress thrown in the back, plus a sign on the window that says "When this van's rockin, don't come knockin".
(b) A flashy gold Opel Manta GTE with body graphics, furry steering wheel cover and a 25 foot CB aerial on the roof.
(c) A small, economic car to drive, with a catalytic converter of course. Preferably something French, like a Renault or Citroen.

7. You're planning a holiday to surprise your girlfriend. Where would take her?

(a) To a 'couples' hotel where you can spend the day ogling women and drinking lager on the beach, the evenings ogling women and drinking lager in the disco, and the early mornings ogling the toilet bowl as you puke your guts up into it.
(b) Treat her to a luxury cruise for a fortnight to give her a break from the cooking and washing up she does for the other 50 weeks of the year.
(c) Fly to Peru then travel overland to Nicaragua to witness the suffering of the indigenous peoples, sending all your friends recycled post cards then arriving at Heathrow six months later with a half a pound of cannabis up your arse.

THERE WAS A LOT OF NOISE COMING FROM YOUR SHOE LAST NIGHT. SINGING AND DANCING 'TILL TWO IN THE MORNING

YES, I'VE GOT A CLUB FOOT

'PC' OF CAKE!

8. You're married and your missus looks after the house. One day she turns round and says she wants to get a job. What would you do?

(a) Slap her and tell her you wear the trousers in your house. No wife of your is going out to work.

(b) Tell her "That's fine, as long as my dinner's on the table when I get home. In fact, the extra money might come in handy".

(c) Show your total support by packing in your own job, going out and buying a pink pinafore, and become a house husband. (Then, when she's at work, sit around watching Australian soaps all day, and discussing the merits of various brands of coffee and washing up powder with the next door neighbour.)

9. If a bird agrees to go to the cinema with you, what would you take her to see?

(a) A saucy British comedy at the local flee pit, starring Robin Askwith and several struggling actresses who have since become famous and who you never imagined in a million years would do a film like that. Like Jill Gascgoine, for example.

Actress Jill Gascgoine - took the Confessions shilling.

(b) Any film with loads of explosions in it, starring a tough bloke with big muscles.

(c) Some foreign film with subtitles at the local 'art house' cinema, starring some ponce like like Gerald Diepardew or whatever he's called.

10. Your partner invites you to a dinner party being thrown by friend of hers. When you get there it turns out the host is a pinch of snuff. How would you react?

(a) Storm out immediately, shouting incoherent homo-phobic abuse, and hurling a stone through the front window as you leave.

(b) Politely excuse yourself, pretending to be unwell, and leave keeping your back to the wall just in case.

(c) Stay all evening and enjoy yourself, regardless of anyone's sexual disposition. But discreetly try to steer-away from subjects like football and girls when talking to the host.

Gerald Deeyepadew - the thinking birds bit of rough.

11. You've been out for the evening and by 11.30pm you find yourself leaning on your girlfriend in the queue at the fish and chip shop. You were feeling dizzy, but you've just thrown up and now you're feeling fine. Well, sort of. Suddenly you notice that another man in the queue is looking at your bird. How do you react?

(a) Stare at him face to face, from half an inch away, and ask him whether he was indeed looking at your bird.

(b) Ask no questions. Just launch into an unprovoked attack accompanied by a barrage of half formed obscenities, until such time as other customers restrain you with cries of "Leave it", "It's not worth it" and "It's just the beer talking".

(c) Tell him that its sexist to look at another bloke's bird, and demand an apology. Or you'll lamp him.

12. You've pulled a classy, high brow bit of crumpet and she's invited you back to her place. Bingo! You're in the bedroom, the kits are off, and you've got the green light. How do you proceed?

(a) Give her a right good three minute scuttling before wiping your cock on the duvet and catching the last bus home.

(b) Give her a right good three minute scuttling then try to stay awake long enough for a fag and a cuddle before you nod off.

(c) Sex should be a beautiful, mutually satisfying, shared experience. So spend at least ten minutes on a bit of foreplay. Then give her a right good three minute scuttling as previously.

How 'New' are you?

Award yourself 1 point for each answer (a), one point for a (b), and two points for each (c). Then tot up your total and see how PC you could be.

24 points: Well done. You're obviously a sensitive, thoughtful, caring individual. You treat everyone – both male and female – as individuals, and you enter into relationships with honesty, maturity and respect for your partner. Birds will go bonkers for a bloke like you, so get straight down to the nearest University Student Union and *fill your boots!*

18 to 23 points: Not bad. But you're still having trouble coming to terms with women as individuals, and not as objects. And you labour under the false impression that women can be impressed by macho behaviour and the show of aggression. Unless you change your way of thinking the high class talent will continue to pass you by. But don't worry. If you lower your sights a bit some old slapper's bound to give you a shag.

12 to 17 points: A poor score. To put it bluntly, you're a male chauvinist pig. You think that women exist merely to serve and to satisfy you. You are shallow, and feel intimidated by any woman who fails to fulfil that subservient role. You'll never get to shag the real dollies at that rate. You'll end up hitched to some ugly boiler.

11 or less: Either you can't add up, or you've missed out at least one question. Go back to the beginning and try again.

How do the TV PC's pull their crumpet? How do television's bobbies on the beat go about bagging a bird?

P.C. Nick Berry, alias actor Simon Wicksy, star of TV's Yorkshire police vet drama 'Heartbeat', confirmed that there wasn't many birds going spare in nineteen sixties rural Yorkshire. "Some nights I end up Heart**beating** my meat, if you know what I mean". But Simon believes one thing gives him the edge over other horny TV cops. "Singing my own them tune in a nancy voice impresses the birds no end", he told us. "They always go for the puffy pop star pin-up type like me. And besides, there's not a great deal of competition in 'Heartbeat'. Birds have only got three bobbies to choose between. Me, Selwyn Froggit and Mr Derek out of Basil Brush, who looks about 90 now."

TV's beer swilling **Inspector Morse**, alias actor John Thaw, relies on a combination of flashiness and sophistication to get his leg over in Oxford, a town bursting at the seems with high class muff. "It's a bit of a cliche, but the big red Mark II Jag is a regular fanny magnet", he told us. However Morse finds that the more sophisticated crumpet – often the ones who perform better in the sack – aren't so easily impressed. "That's why I always talk like I've swallowed a dictionary, and go to opera and stuff. That's for the benefit of the top notch birds, and I've pulled a few of them, I can tell you."

Competition for toosh on the set of one BBC police drama is pretty hot at times, with two top TV detectives battling for birds. For moody tough guy Tyneside detective **Spender**, former TV bricky Oz, alias Geordie actor Freddie Nail, faces fierce competition from former Scarborough beat bobby **P.C. Penrose**, alias TV's 'Rosie', Nail's grey haired senior officer. Viewers might expect Nail to put his hard man image to good use when it comes to tapping the lasses. But former fifteen pints a fight man Freddie, now a respected writer and director, finds that the tricks he learnt as a child are still the most effective. "Showing off never fails," he boasted. "After a busy day of filming on the streets of Newcastle I love to get my bike out of the shed and ride up and down our street doing 'no hands'. If that doesn't impress the girls, I do a few 'wheelies', then skid to a halt right in front of them."

TV's Inspector Regan (left) alias actor Jack Thaw (above)

Freddie has found that another trick which never fails is Sellotaping a lolly stick to the front forks. "When the wheel turns the lolly stick hits the spokes and makes a noise just like a motorbike", said Fred yesterday.

Another hard drinking hard man cop is TV's **Inspector Jack Regan**, alias actor John Thaw, star of hit seventies cop show The Sweeney. John doesn't have much time for political correctness. "I'm a member of the old school. If I want a bird I just kick the door down, shout 'Sweeney', call everyone a bastard, then go down the rub-a-dub and pick up the first slapper I see, give her a good old cattle truck, and then piss off first thing in the morning after growing three days stubble overnight which I shave off while pouring myself a mug of whisky."

Pooar! Was that

A wind of change is blowing through the Kent port of Folkstone since the recent opening of the Channel Tunnel.

But the residents haven't had a whiff of the booming business and economic growth they had expected from their new link to the continent. Instead they are breathing in dense, foggy clouds of putrid garlic fumes which are drifting through the tunnel.

MATTER

And this gas is no laughing matter. For British officials believe their French counterparts are *deliberately* pumping trouser gas through the tunnel in order to solve their own pollution problems. And as a result dangerously high levels of French fart fumes could soon be causing serious environmental damage in the Kent area.

GLOSSER

Engineers at the British end of the tunnel first detected a whiff of pickled eggs the day after the tunnel was officially opened by the Queen. At about the same time several complaints were made from members of the public who noticed that the white cliffs of Dover were turning yellow. Scientific tests then confirmed that alarming levels of guff gases originating on the French side were filtering through the tunnel.

EGGSHELLER

But as well as the obvious dangers to safety, local residents are concerned about the immediate threat which the Chunnel chuff gases pose to the environment. For the unpleasant stench can very quickly erode stone work, cause cars to rust, trees to shed their foliage, and wallpaper to peel off. Farm produce from within a 50 mile radius of the tunnel entrance is being monitored by Ministry of Agriculture officials, and one herd of cattle has already been destroyed after their milk began to taste of mouldy cheese and pickled eggs.

FRENCH

Officially the French deny funnelling their fumes into the Chunnel, but their diet

Farting Frogs funnel chuffs through Chunnel

of thick black coffee, garlic and frog's legs has lead to serious pollution problems in the past. And the French government were known to be investigating new ways of getting rid of the estimated 750 million tons of trouser emissions which the French public let off every day.

CAPITAL

John Major is thought to have expressed his personal concern to the Prime Minister of France over the matter, however, the Channel Tunnel Treaty which was signed by both countries makes no mention of fart gases, and as a result the British authorities are unable to take action over the issue.

RED

How to dispose of their plentiful and particularly pungent cabbage clouds has been a constant problem for the French throughout history. Napoleon first

highlighted the problem in 1812 after his army conquered Moscow only for the city to be burnt down after French troops, celebrating their victory, had accidently ignited their botty burps. Napoleon offered a reward of 2,000 francs (a sum of French money) to anyone who could invent a method of safely disposing of his countrymen's anal emissions.

BLACK

Another attempt to solve the problem came in the shape of the Eiffel Tower which was originally designed as a giant flue to release pump gases into the sky above Paris. But street cafe owners complained that such a scheme would be unhygenic with so many Parisians sitting on the pavement all day drinking coffee and eating garlic bread. And so the tower was converted into a tourist attraction instead.

Scene of the smells – the British entrance to the Channel Tunnel yesterday.

The people of New York were grateful when the French presented them with the Statue of Liberty to commemorate the anniversary of American independence. But unknown to the Americans the statue was in fact intended as a 'Trojan Pump Horse'. It was in fact a cunningly designed giant gas tank filled with odourous farts. The gas would have been burnt off slowly, keeping the statue's famous torch alight for up to fifty years. But the resulting clouds of pungent smoke would have thrown the city into darkness and caused widespread illness and disease. Fortunately for the Americans the statue sprang a leak during its voyage across the Atlantic and the gas escaped, killing millions of fish.

PINK

Only Sweden has ever attempted to tackle the problem of national flatulence. In 1989 they became the first country in Europe to harness pump power and convert it into energy. The

flatulence fired electrical generator station at Trask was the first of its kind in the world, using farts to power a series of giant windmills which would in turn generate electricity. A 'wind tunnel' was built from the densely populated South East of the country to the power station 600 miles away. Unfortunately the amount of fart coming through the tunnel was insufficient to make the giant windmills turn, and the decision was taken to scrap the £400 billion project.

SHIT

Last night British Nuclear Fuels began negotiating with French sewage officials in an attempt to resolve the Channel Tunnel wind problem. It is thought that BNF will buy France's excess emissions and transport them to Nuclear power stations in Britain where they will piss about with them for several years before deciding what the fuck to do next.

These two world famous landmarks were both built as cunning fart disposal devices.

VOUS?

We're farting back for Britain!

We're launching a patriotic campaign to save Britain from the disgusting smell which the French are chunnelling in our direction. And we already have the backing of several top stars, including Jim 'Nick Nick' Davison, Sting, Dame Vera Lynn and the late Field Marshall Montgomery.

We plan to give the Frogs a taste of their own medicine by sending them some good old British farts, 'Dambusters' style. And these will be bouncing bombs with a difference, as Charles Aznavor and co. will soon be finding out.

We're going to inflate red, white and blue beach balls using British wind, and send them bouncing off the white cliffs of Dover towards the French coast. And in a highly emotional atmosphere Dame Vera will sing some of her wartime favourites as the bombs are launched. If the French thought D-Day was spectacular, wait till they see this!

This is how YOU can help. We want everyone in Britain to send us a fart, and we'll use your farts to inflate our bouncing bombs. All you have to do is fart into an envelope, and send it to the following address: Viz 'Fartbusters Campaign', P.O. Box 1PT, Newcastle upon Tyne, NE99 1PT. And remember to mark your envelopes 'Proud to be British'. You can send as many farts as you like, but each one must be in a separate envelope. We

Proud to be pumping for Britain. Jim 'nick nick' Davidson (above) and Dame Vera (above above).

regret that we cannot accept wet ones.

To prevent your fart simply blowing away whilst in the post, each envelope should be weighed down. To do this simply pop a one pound coin into the envelope before sealing it. And make sure you lick your envelope *before* you fart into it, or use a self-sealing envelope. *Under no circumstances attempt to lick a fart filled envelope.*

Always follow the farting code

For reasons of safety always take these simple precautions when farting:

1. Always fart in a well ventilated room, away from children or pets.

2. Never fart near a naked flame, or attempt to ignite a fart.

3. Under no circumstances should you fart whilst suffering from diarrhoea or any similar medical condition. If in doubt consult your doctor.

4. Never hold a fart in – it could make your heart explode.

Soft in the head!

Euro loonies in Brussels are *stiffening up* the rules governing pornography. And they've threatened to BAN British porn – for being too soft!

An overpaid committee of Eurocrats has decided that soft porn in Britain will have to be hardened up, to bring it in line with other soft porn. Dutch soft porn, for example, is considerably harder that soft porn available in Britain. While in France hard porn would be considered soft in Holland.

STANDARD

Now Euro chiefs plan to change all that by introducing standard softness for all European soft porn, and tough new regulations to ensure that hard porn isn't soft.

HEAD

"The idea of hardening up soft porn is quite ridiculous", said soft porn publisher David Sullivan. "Hard porn is more expensive than soft porn, and it would be hard to start making hard porn soft, or harden our soft porn, because we'd have to charge soft porn prices for porn that is essentially hard. The sums wouldn't add up".

DAVEY

The Dutch porn industry is noted for its hard porn, much of which is banned in Britain. Indeed, porn which is hard in Britain is often soft by the time it reaches Amsterdam. In contrast, soft Dutch porn has hardened over the years, and is considered hard on this side of the Channel.

MICKEY

Any move to introduce standard levels of softness and hardness for porn will be

Euro chiefs tell Britain 'Harden up your porn'

Best of British. A saucy girl bends down (left) whilst a buxom brunette reclines next to a central heating radiator (below).

beset by difficulties, as Dr. Leo Svideritch, Professor of Porn Studies at Luton University, told us. "The softness of porn is relative. It depends on who is viewing it.

PETER

Dr Svideritch believed that a ten year programme of porn re-education would be necessary before English voyeurs would be able to

view Dutch soft porn without it appearing hard. "Similarly, our hard porn will continue to be soft until a significant change in porn attitudes occurs", he told us.

MIKE

Across Europe there are different interpretations of hard and soft. Porn isn't like cheese. You cannot measure how soft it is by pressing it with your finger".

JOKE

CIRCUS STILTWALKERS OUTFITTERS

HOWS BUSINESS?

WE'VE BEEN MAKING ENORMOUS STRIDES.

RECENTLY.

58

LeTTeRBoCkS

LETTERBOCKS
Viz, P.O.Box 1PT
Newcastle upon Tyne
NE99 1PT

Kellogs talking out their arse

Impressed by their claim that they 'don't make cereals for anyone else' I purchased a packet of Kelloggs Cornflakes recently. Imagine my dismay when two days later I discovered that my neighbour has a packet also.

Mrs I. Well
Wensleydale

If drugs are such a problem on the streets of Britain why was I arrested at Heathrow airport for trying to smuggle cannabis on a plane to America? Surely I should be congratulated for attempting to take this substance out of the country.

Mr S. Rule
H.M. Prison
Hull

Patches aren't a patch on tabs

I had been trying for several months to give up nicotine patches, without success. Then the other day in the newsagents I discovered highfibre sticks containing the same chemical, for inhalation. These 'ciggies' or 'tabs' are much cheaper than nicotine patches, but have the same satisfying effect. They are available in various brands and strengths and I would recommend them to fellow patch wearers.

B. Carr
Nottingham

Doctors say that drinking beer piles on the weight. That's nonsense. My grandfather drank ten pints a day for forty years and only weighted five stones when he died of liver cancer recently.
These so-called experts don't know what they're talking about.

Ruth Octopus (Mr)
Debenhams

These are my girlfriend's favourite biscuits which I bought in a foreign country recently. Do I win £5?

T. I. Ruler
Cheshire

Congratulations! There's a crisp fiver on its way to you. If anyone else is going abroad, remember to scan those supermarket shelves for rude foreign products. And there's a special £500 prize for the first person who sends us a packet of anything called 'Fannybatter'.

Does he not know that?

Graham Taylor's ignorance beggars belief. In his 'Woodlouse World Cup Game' (Viz, last issue) he incorrectly refers to woodlice as 'insects'. Woodlice belong to the order Isopoda within the class Malacostraca, part of the phylum Crustacea. Insects all belong to the phylum Uniramia. Clearly this man is not even fit to manage a team of woodlice. Heaven help Wolverhampton Wanderers.

D. Bentley
Radcliffe, Manchester

Here we go again

Reading the last issue it occurred to me, why don't you pad out the stories a bit so that a cartoon (Cockney Wanker for example) takes up three pages instead of one or two. I'm sure the readers will be so busy laughing at all the funny bits they won't notice that there's less and less in each issue. And while you're at it, why not add a few more pages of adverts for good measure.

Mark Hopkinson
Leeds

Do any other readers know this bloke Mark Hopkinson? Perhaps you've got a school photo of him when he was little, preferably looking stupid. We'll pay £25 for any embarrassing photo of him that we print. And we'd also like to hear from his ex-girlfriends. What was he like in bed? Write and let us know. We'll pay £25 for any dirt we publish in the next issue.

We can learn a lot about ourselves by studying nature and other living creatures with which we share our planet. For instance, birds have hollow bones. And if you stick a monkey's hand in a naked flame it will try and bite you.

Dr J. Nettleton
Whitstable, Kent

Another sad bastard

Regarding your 'London Bus competition' (issue 66) the bus featured in the movie 'Summer Holiday' was in fact an AEC Regent and *not* a Routemaster as you implied.

Roger Dowsall
Doncaster

Well spotted Roger. And thanks also to the dozens of Star Trek fans who wrote in and pointed out various inaccuracies in our 'Derek Anorak' cartoon strip. I'm afraid there's no prizes for anyone, but perhaps you could invite Roger to your next 'Treky' convention and he could show you some slides of buses or something.

In reply to your unusual picture request offer (issue 66) how about a picture of Susan Hampshire, in a bra, feeding monkeys bananas?

Mrs I. Rapeseed-Oil
Finsbury Park

Here you are Mrs Rapeseed-Oil. That picture took quite some finding, and you came very close to pocketing our £100 prize. Better luck next time. In the meantime here's a reminder to other readers. Send us your unusual picture requests, and if we can't find the photo you're after, we'll pay you £100. Send your requests – anything at all – to '£100 Picture Challenge' at the usual address.

Kippers

Would any of your readers interested in forming a Kipper Appreciation Society please do so without my help, as I am a member of the Kipper Appreciation League and therefore have no wish to join a rival group.

J. Mayor
Sutton

Arses

In reply to your request for big arses in the last issue, how about this cafe I spotted while abroad on holiday. God knows which country it was in. They all look pretty much the same once you get off the ferry.

John Wobkel
Wood Green

British banks go out of their way to try and persuade students to open accounts, but how about this for the bank that likes to lick arse. I spotted this genuine bank sign in Turkey.

Jonathan Wilson
Huddersfield

Those arses are all well and good but you said the prize would go to the biggest arse. Well, how about this road sign spotted in Switzerland Surely I win.

S. Baker
Billinghurst
West Sussex

Congratulations, Your arse is the biggest and so S. Baker collects our top prize of £20. A tenner each goes to the runners up.

A load of wank

I am a resident of the german town of Wank and consequently am able to make a tidy living sending small minded British publications photographs of our name sign. Here you are. Do I win £5?

P. Matthaus
Wank

A pair of arseholes

In the last issue we asked you to send in pictures of Viz look-a-likes and we offered £25 or something like that for every picture we used. As we were judging your pictures it became apparent that there should be a new category, that of Daftest

Looking Twat Holding Up A Copy Of Viz. Here are the top two entries, Stuart Hooper of Ilford and Norm from Ivybridge, Devon. Gary Hooper and Andrew Elliot each win £25 for sending in the snaps.

Cockney wankers

Meanwhile our £100 prize for Cockney Wanker look-a-like goes to Graham Boxall of Beckenham, Kent, who sent this picture in of his mate.

The runner-up was Steve White of World Courier, whose mug shot was sent in by his mates in the transport department (who get to keep the money).

Daft bastard

Aileen McKee of Glasgow sent us this photo and reckons her mate Jillian looks like Spoilt Bastard. We're going to bend the rules a little on this one Aileen, and print the picture but not send you any money.

«Top Tips»

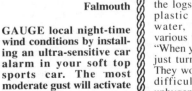

MOTORISTS. Make distant oncoming drivers think you're possibly driving a Volvo by leaving your side lights on during the day.

P. Delaney
Greenhills, Dubin

READ small print easily and without the use of expensive glasses by looking at books through a pint glass full of cider.

E. C.
Leeds

DOG owners. Next time your dog does a 'soft one' on the beach annoy metal detector owners by dropping nuts and bolts into it and then covering it in sand.

L. O'Hara
Inverness

RE-CREATE the fairground thrills of the waltzer in your own home by simply drinking 12 cans of Carlsberg Special then asking a couple of friends to stand at the end of your bed and occasionally give it a shove as you try to get to sleep.

S. Leone
Moffat

PENSIONERS. Don't forget to retire to bed before 8pm so that you'll be able to get up at the crack of dawn tomorrow and go and collect your morning paper while anyone with any sense is still sound asleep in bed.

D. Lynch
Quarter

SEAGULLS. Fly upside down next time you're over Cornwall. I can assure you it isn't even worth shitting on.

I. Ashenden
Falmouth

GAUGE local night-time wind conditions by installing an ultra-sensitive car alarm in your soft top sports car. The most moderate gust will activate the alarm and keep both yourself and your neighbours fully informed as to local wind conditions.

M. Retard
Cambridge

LADIES. When commuting to work try leaving the house five minutes earlier than usual in order that male commuters may be spared the ridiculous spectacle of you attempting to 'run' for a train.

Eric Hoggers
Hayes, Middlesex

IMPROVE your eye/hand co-ordination by attempting to 'bomb' ants on the pavement with small ball bearings.

Tim Erroll
Romford, Essex

NEWSAGENTS. Increase your profits by stocking VIZ on a lower shelf, instead of shoving it up on the top shelf. This would enable short people to buy it as well. It may be a pile of wank, but it isn't a wank mag.

D. Hammond
Potters Bar

LADIES. When driving to work try getting out of bed ten minutes earlier. This will enable you to put your make-up on using the bathroom mirror, and not in the rear view mirror of your car whilst sitting at a green traffic light.

A. Compass
Red Leicestershire

STAR SHIT ENTERPRISE

An unemployed Bolton man plans to go where no businessman has gone before by launching a pioneering enterprise of his own.

Harold Biggins plans to make a fortune selling souvenirs of the stars, despite the fact that his products are shit. Quite literally! For Harold intends to market celebrity excrement, buying stools fresh from the stars, and selling them as paper weights.

METEOR

"I'm surprised nobody had thought of the idea before", Harold told us. "It seems such an obvious money earner. Turds which would otherwise have simply been flushed down the toilet can be taken away and sold to fans. I'm sure there'll be huge demand, especially for someone like George Michael or Sting's shit."

ASTEROID

Originally Harold had planned to make 'Celebrity Stool Snow Storms' with the logs, sealing them in a plastic dome filled with water, but there were various technical problems. "When you shook them they just turned into diarrhoea. They would have been very difficult to market, and unhygenic if they cracked." So instead he plans to encase them in glass, along with a signed picture of the star responsible for the dump.

HAEMORHOID

Already a host of celebrities have donated droppings after Harold began visiting them to explain his scheme. "Generally the people I've spoken to have been very helpful", said Harold. "I just turn up on their doorsteps with my plastic bag and a spoon. Early morning is the best time, as that seems to be when most of the stars carry out their ablutions. There's the odd awkward customer who refuses to help, but generally speaking they've been marvellous: Cliff Richard, for example, even had one ready in a bag for me when he opened the door."

ADENOID

Unfortunately Harold's bank manager has been less than helpful. "He put me in touch with their Small Businesses Adviser, but when I explained my idea the only advice I got was to "fuck off". And without financial backing I can't get the business off the ground."

POLAROID

Unless the bank have a change of heart Harold fears he may have to throw away the dozen or so stools he has so far collected. "My wife won't let me keep them in the house, so I've got them all in the back yard at the minute. But there's a limit to how long you can keep them before they go all crumbly. They're already drying out."

POLAR BEAR

"The biggest one I've got so far was from Meatloaf. It's a bit on the big side for a paper weight, but it would make a good door stopper. However, if I don't get something sorted out soon I'm going to have to chuck it out, and that will mean having to break it up, which would be a shame.

ONE SMALL STEP FOR

'One small step' was how American space man Neil Armstrong described first setting foot on the moon.

But now, as America celebrates the 25th anniversary of those mortal words, one other man is accusing the man who spoke them of being a **LIAR** and a **CHEAT**. Indeed those history books may have to be re-written. For according to a man we met in the pub, it was a **MONKEY** who had already became the first man on the moon, two years earlier.

By our
Science Correspondent
Dr. Stanley Jordan

MONKEY

The man, who preferred not to be named, said that the monkey was one of several animals the Russians had launched on experimental space flights during the sixties. Previously it was assumed they had all died in space, but unknown to the Russians several dogs and monkeys managed to successfully land their Saturn Five rockets on the moon. And one monkey even managed to return to Earth to get some bananas.

MOONshot
The moon may look as small as a tennis ball in the sky, but in real life it would be the size of a sprout, if the Earth was a football.

However the monkey's rocket crash landed in the man's back garden, and the space monkey has been living in his garden shed ever since.

WATER MARGIN

According to the man whilst on the moon the dogs and monkeys bread, creating a new kind of space monkey called a mog. "They have long tails, and are

MOONshot
The Dark Side of the Moon was a best selling album by Pink Floyd which stupid hippies often listened too lying on the floor with their eyes shut.

very friendly", he told us. And he said that the monkey was now prepared to go public and tell its story for the first time. "It's silver", he said "and it talks a special moon monkey language".

The man offered to take us to his shed and show us the monkey for £25. However after leaving the pub and wandering around for several moments he told us he'd forgotten where he lived.

Later he became unsteady on his feet and sat down on a grass verge where he attempted to offer us a drink from a large bottle of cider wrapped in brown paper. He then fell asleep.

It was one giant leap for monkeykind

Scientists interview the first space monkeys (above) and Neil Armstrong (right) steps foot on the moon whilst Buz Aldridge watches.

Where are they now?

Neil Armstrong returned to Earth a hero after his heroic moon mission. American Presidents queued up to shake his hands. But twenty-five years later his space travelling days are over, and nowadays you're more likely to catch Armstrong reaching for The Sun, The Star... or the Leicester Mercury, at his newsagents shop in Wigston, Leicestershire.

Like the moon Neil, now 47, rises early in the morning to open his shop and get the papers ready for delivery. He admits he misses space travel, especially taking man's

The crew of Apollo Eleven (right). Left to right (clockwise) Shepherd (right), Glen and Armstrong (left of picture on right)

first step on the moon, but nowadays he's more than happy with his work.

"I have a nice little shop and some very nice customers. I occasionally miss the excitement of the rocket launches, the splash downs and the sticky tape welcomes, but I'm happy with what I do. I don't regret hanging up my space boots".

Neil's colleagues on Apollo Eleven, David Shepherd and Glenn Close, are more reluctant to sever their links with

space, although their careers as space men ended many years ago.

COMEDY

They now tour variety clubs and holiday camps as comedy double act 'The Astronutties'.

"They used to believe that lunatics were driven mad by the moon", said Glenn yesterday. "Well, I guess that's what happened to us. Because we're absolutely crackers!"

DRAMA

"To see our act, anyone would think we were completely mad. And they'd probably be right", chuckled Shepherd. "Your readers

should come and see us. We'd be *over the moon* if they did", he quipped. The Astronutties can be seen at the Pier Theatre, Great Yarmouth, for the remainder of the summer season. Tickets are still available at all prices from the booking office, as well as at the door on the night.

MOONshot
In a well known nursery rhyme a cow jumped over the moon. But in reality a cow cannot even jump over a football.

MOONshot
The moon may be as big as a sprout, but it weighs less than a tomato, due to the weightless atmosphere in space.

A LIAR

Who's loony boozer Moon was where when man first set foot on moon?

We all remember vividly where we were and what we were doing on that historic day in 1969 when man first stepped onto the moon. So we decided to ask a few stars where they were, and what they were doing, on that day 25 years ago.

And who better to start with than with The Who. Their drummer always had a reputation for **lunacy,** so we asked Keith Moon what he recalled of the occassion.

SPORT

Speaking from his plush £190,000 Oxfordshire grave Moon was remaining tight lipped yesterday. "I really don't have anything to say. I'm dead at the minute. Can you call back tomorrow?"

COBBER

Sacha Distel was another celebrity keeping his cards close to his chest. We rang him at his home outside Paris and asked whether any raindrops had fallen on his head on that famous day back in 1969. "I'm sorry. I don't recall. Say anything you want", he told us.

Boozy Moon - Who loony

Actor David Niven is a man with moon connections, having named his best selling auto-biography 'The Moon's A Balloon'. So where was he when man first ventured onto the moon's surface. We asked his agent. "I'm afraid David is dead as well" he told us, "and there are no plans for him to be alive again in the near future".

The moon and the stars

The stars of popular music have always sung about the moon. Indeed, along with the sun, and perhaps Mars, the moon is one of space's most often sung about planets.

Songs like The Police's *Walking On The Moon* and Mike Oldfield's sister's *Moonshadow* have ensured that over the years the moon has never been far from pop's top ten.

Las Vegas Elvis (right) – wanted the moon and the Kings pyramid theory (below)

MOON

But for one star for whom the moon meant more than most people, to, was Las Vegas Elvis. For the bloated former King of Rock and Roll lived, breathed and slept moon. And he believed, in his crazy, drug distorted mind, that one day the moon would be his.

SUN

After binging on fast food and drugs Elvis hatched a crazy plot to kidnap the moon and keep it in a giant cupboard. Combining a scant knowledge of Egyptian mythology and a fascination with James Bond gadgetry, he planned to launch a giant cigar shaped rocket that would open up at the end and literally 'swallow' the moon whole.

MIRROR

Elvis believed the moon was like a Malteeser, with a honeycombe centre made out of gold. He was convinced the Egyptians knew this and had built the pyramids to act as a giant space weather vane, pointing the way to the gold. After taking drugs he noticed that if a line was drawn from the top of every pyramid to the moon, all of those lines would converge at the same place. The moon.

Sadly, Elvis's dream to capture the moon and put it in his cupboard never came true. His space programme was besieged with technical problems, and Elvis died, on the lavatory, a drug addict, a bloated shadow of his former self, incontinent, in a nappy, never having seen his space rocket completed.

MOON*shot*

It's impossible for space men to shit in a bucket on the moon. In the weightless atmosphere a turd would simply float out of their bottom and into space.

Hunt for Hunt over

A woman who bought Gareth Hunt at a car boot sale for 20p has been told she cannot keep the former Avengers star.

SIGNAL

Tina Anderson had no idea who Hunt was when she bought him at a car boot sale near her home in Sandal, Cheshire. "I just liked the look of him. I had no idea who he was," she told reporters. But when she took her bargain to Sotherby's to have him valued for insurance purposes, she was surprised to discover that she was the new owner of a former seventies heart throb.

MANOEUVRE

However, her joy was short lived. For Thames Television bosses have stepped in and told Tina that Hunt belongs to them and she must hand the actor back or face legal action. Hunt was reported stolen when he went missing from the back of a van outside Thames Television's Teddington Lock studios in 1978.

CHARLES NOT F
ON TH

A sensational new book by contro-versial author Andrew Raith-Rovers has lifted the toilet lid on goings on inside the Buckingham Palace throne room.

The book has been written with the blessing of Princess Diana, who is eager to win back public support in the light of Charles' recent frank TV interview. She is hoping that smutty revelations about her husband's toilet habits will dirty his Royal reputation, and boost her own popularity.

POTTY

In the following exclusive extract from the book 'Royals On The Throne', Mr Stenhousemuir reveals how the future King of England was never properly potty trained by his parents, which may explain some of the problems he has gone on to suffer in later life.

LOONY

❝ The Queen and Prince Phillip took very little interest in their eldest son's toilet training. It was left to Lord Mountbatten, Charles' favourite uncle, to teach the future King how to use the potty.

CRAZY

In many ways the young Charles was never able to live up to his father's expectations, and he considered himself a failure.

By our Royal Correspondent Madam Cholet

But it was with enormous pride that shortly after his fourth birthday he took his father by the hand and lead him up to the toilet. There, pointing at a clump of excrement and wet toilet tissue lying on the floor, he proudly announced that he had wiped his own bottom for the first time.

BLOCK

That may have been Charles' first toilet mishap, but it was just the latest in a line of Royal lavatorial blunders stretching back through history.

TACKLE

Queen Victoria spent longer on the throne than any other monarch. Indeed, it was often said that she had permanent red seat marks on the back of her legs. She would go for a dump at 11 o'clock every morning, and not re-appear until tea time. Throughout the day dozens of books and tray upon tray of tea and sandwiches

Young Prince missed toilet with his first attempt

Queen Victoria (above) - not amused and the queen mum (right) - ran out of bog roll

would be taken to her in her own private lavatory.

FOUL

One day she tried to get up and couldn't. Her arse had become stuck in the toilet seat. Eventually a team of Royal carpenters were summoned to remove the seat from her arse. However, Victoria refused to let them near her until they covered their eyes. Rarely can there have been a more bizarre scene than the spectacle of Queen Victoria jammed in the lavatory surrounded by four blind-folded carpenters all taking turns at trying to remove the seat from her bottom.

PENALTY

So delighted was the Queen when the seat was eventually prized free from her buttocks, she rewarded the successful carpenter with a knighthood. But a few years later a toilet roll manu-facturer found that Queen Victoria was most certainly not amused by an incident involving a sheet of his tissue paper.

During a routine visit to the toilet she began wiping her arse when the unthinkable happened. Her Royal finger went through the paper with the inevitable consequences. She remained in the bath-room for two weeks scrubbing her fingernail with a stiff brush and carbolic acid. When she eventually emerged she summoned the manu-facturer responsible for the weak toilet roll to the Palace, and chopped his head off with an axe.

Di saw Queen Mum's bum eyesore

When her Royal engage-ment was announced Diana Spencer was suddenly faced with the realisation that she would one day become the Queen of England. But much sooner than that she came face to face with the unacceptable side of Royal lavatorial behaviour.

GOAL

The Queen Mother is notorious for not checking to see if there's any loo roll left before opening the bomb hatch. On this particular occasion she'd just let go of an enormous log when she realised there was no paper to wipe with. So she hitched up her skirt and hobbled downstairs, knickers round her ankles, to get a new roll from the kitchen cupboard. At that moment Diana walked into the kitchen just in time to see a dirty great unwiped

arse staring up at her from the cupboard under the sink.

EVENING

Rumours that Diana suffers from the slimmer's disease bolivia nirvana are untrue. The plain truth is that she is haunted by that picture of the Queen Mum's backside, and to this day she cannot bring herself to eat anything cooked in the Palace kitchen.

WINNING

Events over the years have shown that there is a constant need to review Royal security arrange-ments. But if there's one thing that a Royal fears more than a crazed gunman jumping out of a crowd, it's the dreaded turtle's head poking out their backside half way through a Royal walk-about.

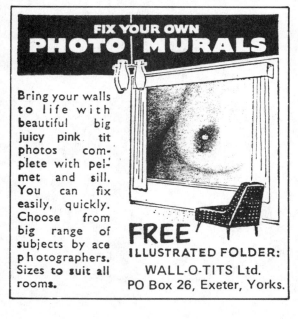

T TO SHIT
E THRONE

Bono no-nos
so-so
go-go
pogo
dodo
Jo-Jo

Bono - mono photo

Irish rocker Bono has pulled the plug on plans for a multi million pound musical based on the demise of the Dodo, only weeks before the production was due to be staged in the West End.

The U2 star withdrew his backing for the show in a row over casting of the lead role. It is thought he was unhappy with the mediocre performances of the female lead, former go-go dancer Jo-Jo Wood, wife of the Rolling Stones' Ronnie. Jo-Jo had been chosen to play the part of a Dodo and had to perform in a full dodo costume. Bono had also insisted that the entire cast perform on pogo sticks.

FIELD

Meanwhile a former tramp in the woodwind section of the orchestra began a work to rule last night and refused to play an unaccompanied section of the

Hobo's yoyo
Cocoa oboe
solo go-slow

musical score in protest at the fluctuating prices charged by the production caterers for his favourite bedtime drink. "On Monday I was charged 30p for a mug of Cocoa", he told us. "Yet on Tuesday they were charging 50p. When I complained on Friday they said I could have it for 20p. It's ridiculous".

Charles - shat on the floor

Strict security means that when nature calls Diana or Charles cannot just pop into the nearest public lavatory, and even in these modern times it would be totally unacceptable for them to nip into someone's garden and go behind a bush. Intricate plans must be made, and security checks carried out not only on the lavatories, but also in the cisterns and down the 'U' bend. As a result every stool must be planned at least six months in advance, and the Royals must stick to a strict timetable of ablutions.

LOSING

Royal toilet discipline is at its toughest during overseas state visits. It is a custom that the Royals must never defecate on foreign soil, for to do so would be an insult to the host head of state. This can cause enormous

discomfort bearing in mind some of the foreign food that they have to eat. For no matter how badly they need a shit, they cannot let it out until they get back on board the Royal yacht Britannia.

DRAWING

Plans to retire the Royal yacht have caused unprecedented flatulence among the Royals. They fear that in future they could spend days on end having to be being nice to foreigners, while at the same time clasping their bum cheeks firmly together in an attempt to hold onto a particularly loose stool. **9**

Tomorrow: Charles lets slip a rogue number two during a visit to Australia, but somehow manages to keep his cool as it tumbles down his trouser leg and is quickly trodden on by security guards.

BOTTY
BURGLARS

'Cheeky' thieves have made off with a collection of arses from a country house in Gloucestershire.

PAINTING

Their haul of over fifty arses, valued at around £40,000, includes the late Arthur Askey's arse, plus one buttock believed to have been Napoleon's.

WELL

The private collector, who preferred not to be named, has offered a reward of £5,000 for the return of the arses.

TOPS ARE
TOP
says George

Britain's flagging fashion industry was rocked to its foundations last night after a bizarre outburst by outspoken pop gender bender Boy George.

Former heroin addict and 'A' Team star George, whose hits dried up some time ago, **SLAMMED** British designers and accused them of creating clothes that were too complex.

DRUM

The controversial singer, whose hits include 'Karma Karma Karma Karma Karma Chameleon', is reported to have said that designers should get back to basics

George - simple tops

such as "nice simple tops", in an interview about five years ago.

PAD

We thought about ringing unhinged fashion guru Vivian Westwood for a couple of potty comments, but decided that on reflection it probably wasn't a good idea.

BLIMEY! WHAT A FIND

The farmer who discovered Tommy Steele in a disused barn at his farm in Cumbria is today £20,000 richer after the vintage actor and singer was sold at auction yesterday.

Sam Armstrong uncovered the veteran star among piles of straw while clearing out derelict buildings at a farm near Penrith which had previously belonged to his father.

BARN

"I had no idea who he was at first until we pulled him out of the barn and dusted him off", Mr Armstrong told reporters yesterday. But a quick examination revealed that the veteran star was in remarkably good condition. "Someone has painted him pink, and quite a few bits and pieces were missing, but we got quite a surprise when we tried starting him up and he began singing and dancing first time", said Mr Armstrong.

SCHOOL

Enquiries revealed that Mr Armstrong's grandfather had bought Steele in the mid

Blimey! What a find he's got

What a great big find

EXCLUSIVE

Farmer Sam (left) with his dog and Tommy Steel (right) - found in barn

seventies from a fairground in Perthshire where he had been converted for use as a sword dancer. "After my grandfather died he must have simply been forgotten about and left in the barn to rust".

BACK

And while the remarkable find has meant a surprise financial windfall for Sam, there is also good news for fans of the singer who's best known hit was 'The Little White Bull'. For the star has been bought by members of the Tommy Steele Society and they plan to have him fully restored, singing and dancing live on stage, within five years. But the restoration work could prove to be expensive, as their secretary Bill Walsh explains.

SQUARE

"Unfortunately, Tommy's bowler hat and cheeky grin were missing when he was found. But we have already been in touch with one manufacturer in Poland who still makes that type of hat and we are confident of finding a suitable replacement grin, even if it means commissioning a new one from scratch. There is still a foundry in Shropshire equipped to cast a grin. The only problem is it costs a lot of money".

TRIANGLE

On top of the £20,000 already raised to purchase the star, Bill expects to spend a further £20,000 restoring him to his original condition. And he said the Tommy Steele Society would be grateful for any financial help that the public were willing to give.

ELDORADO

In 1982 the sixties singer Joe Brown was restored to full working order after being found in use as an advertising sign on a roundabout near Leeds. He is now a part of the National Collection and can regularly be seen on TV and making public appearances around the country.

Collins dug up

A farm labourer looking for a piece of a tractor may have uncovered the remains of seventies TV actor Lewis Collins.

Following the find in a field in Suffolk an actor, believed to be Collins, has been sent to the University of Warwickshire for scientific identification. If his identity is confirmed farm labourer Jim Marsden, who discovered the hard man actor, could be in line for a six figure reward.

Collins, star of TV's Professionals, has been preserved by dry clay which surrounded him. Mr Marsden was out searching for a missing bolt which had fallen from his tractor the previous day when he uncovered the actor using a metal detector.

If Collins is declared treasure trove then Mr Marsden will be free to sell the star and keep the proceeds. The last time a seventies TV detective came up for auction was in 1988 when Peter Wingard, star of the Jason King TV series, was sold to a private collector in Japan for £475,000 after being discovered rolled up in an attic in Kent.

LET US PAY

An unholy row has broken out over Church of England plans to introduce 'pay as you pray' meters in households throughout Britain.

The Archbishop of Canterbury, speaking last week, said that a system of metering was necessary because people's praying habits are changing. "More and more people are staying away from church and doing they're prayers at home", he told a top conference of bishops, vicars and vergers in Bournemouth.

CHRISTIANS

He blamed the trend away from church-going on D.I.Y. superstores and the fact that a great many Christians didn't want to miss Little House On The Prairie. And he warned that the church would have to adapt to fit in with new lifestyles.

LIONS

"By praying at home people are avoiding the collection plate, and that is hitting God where it hurts most, in the wallet", he told the conference. Church profits were down for the third consecutive year, he reported, and so a metering system was being considered as a possible solution.

GLADIATORS

If the scheme goes ahead a prayer meter would be installed in every household in Britain and this would record the amount of prayers being done. The local vicar would then come round for tea, and to read the meter. A quarterly bill would be sent to each household, followed two weeks later by a red reminder. Any household who failed to pay for their prayers would then be cut off from God.

TROJANS

Already a pilot scheme introduced in one Parish on the Isle of Wight has proved a success, according to church officials. The scheme, which has been operating for six months, has already raised over half a million pounds towards the local steeple restoration fund. But local residents aren't happy with the new arrangements.

DUREX

Sheila Foster was cut off from God after refusing to pay a £700 bill for prayers she claims she didn't make. "I got a bill for a prayer I was supposed to have made to the little baby Jesus. I

Two vicars calculate prayer bills yesterday

queried it because I hadn't done any prayers that week, but they sent me a final demand then cut me off."

MATES

Sheila is one of many Christians who are leaving the C of E in protest. "Now I've been connected up to the Jews, and they've been really great. They offer cheap rates at weekends, and you can even pray in the garden on Saturdays", she told us.

JIFFY

Another dissatisfied customer is 62 year old Ralph Henderson who has been with the Church of England all his life. "I had a friend staying with me for a few days and one day while I was at work he prayed for a sick relative in Australia during peak rates. When I got the bill I almost shit myself", said Ralph. "They sent a bishop round to check the meter but they still insisted I had to pay". Unable to find the money Ralph was cut off, and faces a winter alone without prayers.

HAND

"My wife only died last year, and I used to pray for her every night. Now I won't even be able to say Grace before my Christmas dinner", said a teary eyed Ralph yesterday.

CARRIER

Miriam Bigfatarsehole, spokeswoman for OffGod, the independent prayer watchdog, said that pensioners would suffer most under

the proposed system. "Old people need to prayer more than most of us, because they're obviously old, and they're going to die soon, and naturally they don't want to go to Hell. By sending them these enormous bills the Church are effectively condemning them to drown in a lake of eternal fire."

HOMING

A Government spokeswoman last night said it had no immediate plans to introduce VAT on prayer bills, although the Chancellor of the Exchequer has so far refused to rule it out. Meanwhile, the Archbishop of Canterbury defended plans for TV advertising campaign for God. He said that the proposed payment of £8 million to Bob Hoskins for a series of two commercials was 'money well spent'.

Hoskins - £15 million

The stumpy headed actor will dress up as a vicar, talk in a cockney accent and pull a funny face at the end of two thirty second TV ads.

Bid to curb bee sex

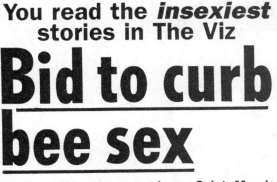

Doddery TV porn campaigner Saint Mary's Lighthouse is to ban sex between bees in her garden.

The wrinkly prune who has devoted her lifetime to complaining about sex and bad language on the box and getting on everyone's tits, has now turned her attention to the humble bumble bee.

WINDOWS

Sickened by sordid scenes the wizened old hag has witnessed through binoculars from her French patio windows, she plans to put an end to all sex between insects in the garden.

VOLUME

"There was a time when gardens were a place where children could play, and old people could sit and fall asleep. But now everywhere you turn there are bees romping about naked, spunking up pollen and fingering their little bee fannies."

TONE

"The men bees are the worst", she continued, "coming at the poor little lady bees with their great big bee cocks in their hands, and dirty, leering grins on their faces. Roughly man handling the poor lady bees into flowers where they commit foul and unthinkable sex acts some of which, frankly, defy belief", she said yesterday.

BASS

Saint Mary's Lighthouse, who is 94, was today in hospital being treated for

'Hive had enough' says leathery faced pointy glasses TV sex campaigner

St. Mary's lighthouse - bee stings

bee stings after being found wandering naked and confused in her garden late last night.

Short hair

Hair cuts will be short in the spirit world, according to Christian pop singer Cliff Richard.

TREBLE

Cliff predicts short hairstyles will be the fashion 'on the other side', and that long hair will not be allowed in heaven, except for Jesus. Facial hair will be frowned upon also. "Only tidy beards like Noel Edmonds and Jeremy

Beadle will be allowed", Cliff told a hairdressing conference in Swindon yesterday.

Gary Bluto On The Box

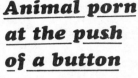

The TV critic who gives it to you straight

These sicko queers ruin our telly

Anyone watch Wimbledon this year? What a bore. I blame the dykes.

You could dig up better looking women in Fred West's back garden. I'd rather go plane spotting in Lockerbie than watch lesbians playing tennis.

Centre Court attendances are down. Hardly surprising. Who in their right mind is going to pay good money to sit and watch a pair of lesbians knock a ball back and forward over a net.

All the excitement at Wimbledon will come in the showers afterwards. It must get pretty hot in there. Hotter than a barbecue in Fred West's back garden. Mind you, I'd rather watch paint peel in the Kings Cross tube disaster than watch sexual perverts cavorting in the showers.

No daughter of mine will ever play tennis. What parent in their right mind is going to allow their young daughter to engage in a physical activity with a bunch of sexual perverts? You've got more chance of finding your baggage in Lockerbie than you have of finding a straight girl on the tennis circuit these days. *I'd rather send my kids pot holing up Julian Clary's backside in Lockerbie.*

★ ★ ★ ★ ★ ★ ★ ★ ★ ★ ★ ★ ★

On the subject of gays, there must be about as much chance of Julian Clary gripping a pencil in his bum cheeks as there is of watching ten minutes of your favourite soap nowadays without a gay appearing on the screen. Gays here, lesbians there. They're popping up as often as stiffs in Fred West's back garden. There's even puffs in Emmerdale now. No wonder the ratings are dropping quicker than bodies in Lockerbie.

What parent in their right mind is going to allow their kids to watch sexual perverts cavorting on their TV screens? *It's about as healthy as unprotected sex with*

Brucey - He's no queer

Julian Clary on the car deck of the Herald of Free Enterprise.

When will the TV bosses learn that sodomy kills? If they had their way they'd all be buggering our kids in the playground at school. I'd rather send my kids rally driving with Ayrton Senna than allow them to be buggered in the playground.

What parent in their right mind would bugger their own kids in their back garden in Lockerbie? They come over here, they take the jobs. I'd rather watch paint dry up Julian Clary's backside. Take our women too. I wouldn't fancy being Fred West's gardener. I'd rather pay Hitler's gas bill. I know what I'd do with them. Put 'em all on a plane and send 'em back to where they came from. *Via Lockerbie.*

Tomorrow: Gary gives a five star review to Brucey's Play Your Cards Right.

Computers set to byte the dust

All computers are set to be banned if a Tory backed bill designed to stop computer porn becomes law.

The Computers and Bizarre Sex Acts Bill has been put forward by Tory MP Sir Anthony Regents-Park in an attempt to curb the current trend of computer pornography. The bill would make it an offence for any person to own or use any form of computer, other than a small electronic calculator.

PRESS

At a press conference yesterday a police officer demonstrated how it was possible to manipulate images on a computer screen for pornographic purposes. He showed members of the press how it was possible to take a harmless image of a chicken and distort it by giving it a huge donkey's cock, and then by simply pressing a button it was possible to make the chicken stick its donkey's cock up a pig's arse, again and again and again.

Animal porn at the push of a button

He then gave the pig huge tits, and made it rub them with its little piggy hands, before a sheep, with a horse's knob, joined in the fun. After a few minutes things were really hotting up. The pig and the sheep were joined by a herd of horny cattle for a farmyard sex orgy which included a lesbian show between two bulls who had been given pigs' tits and big hairy badgers' fannies.

STARCH

At the end of the demonstration Sir Anthony Regents-Park, whose suggestion it was that the bulls should have tits, congratulated police on their efforts.

MRS MILLS

In issue 67 of Viz magazine in an article about carpets, motorbike and crocodiles we referred to the late popular music pianist Mrs Mills as a 'fat cow'. We would like to point out that in so doing it was never our intention to imply that Mrs Mills was either fat, or a cow.

We should like to take this opportunity to apologise for any misunderstanding or offence which may have been caused.

CHEESE PLEASE

Britain's housewives are not afraid to ask for cheese, according to a report out today.

WIN £5 CASH PLAYING BIG MONEY

SNAP!

With TV's RODNEY BEWES

CROSS THE ✗ NIPPLE

YOUR UNIQUE PERSONAL SNAP! CARD IS PRINTED BELOW

MR. PIG the BUTCHER

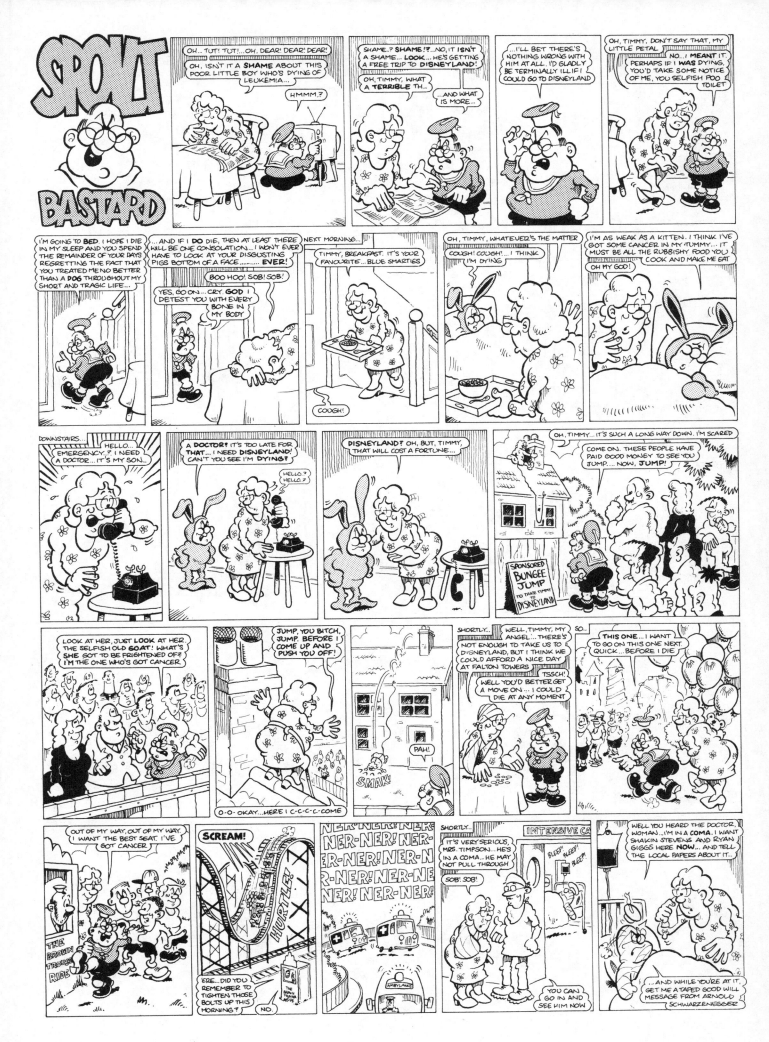

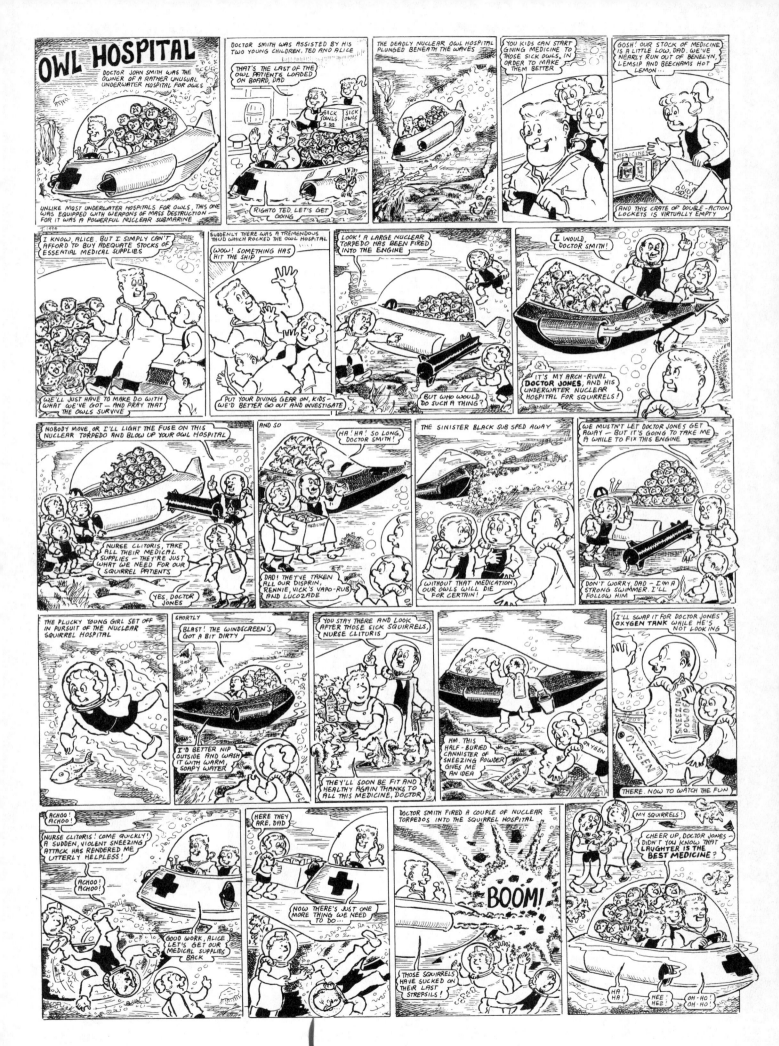

LetterBocks

Slippers slip up

Market traders in our local high street please note. The apostrophe in "Slipper's £1.99" should not be there. A possessive apostrophe is used to indicate when an item or items belong to a person or object. For instance, *Jim's* slippers belong to Jim. Your tatty fluorescent sign would therefore imply that the slippers *own* £1.99. If you wish to advertise something in the plural, simply append the letter 's' to the end of the word, e.g. Slippers.

Miss N. Picker
Berwick

Twenty-two years ago when I first met my wife she was going out with the singer Brian Ferry. Well, if Mr Ferry happens to be reading this he can fucking well have her back now.

A.T.
Newcastle

My wife next whore

As a married man I used to fantasise about the thrill of having sex with a prostitute, but I never dared try it. Well now I get the best of both worlds. First, I put a red bulb in my wife's bedside lamp, then told her to chew gum and appear disinterested during sex. She charges me £20 for hand relief (£30 topless), and £50 for full sex. Our love life has never been so exciting. In order to add a little extra authenticity my 18 year old son acts as her 'pimp', calling her his 'bitch', keeping most of the money and interrupting our 'sessions' if they run slightly over time.

Mr S. Birch
Croydon

LETTERBOCKS
Viz, P.O.Box 1PT
Newcastle upon Tyne
NE99 1PT·

On your Marks

Regarding Mark Hopkinson, the bloke from Leeds who was slagging Viz off in the last issue. He sounds like a Mark Hopkinson I once dated. I was his first girlfriend. I remember him well, as his penis was smaller than a cocktail sausage and he only had one testicle. As I recall he could never get a hard-on, and I'm certain that he was a pillow biter. The last time I saw him he was standing outside a dirty bookshop in Leeds reading some smutty shirt-lifter's rag. He was by far and away the worst shag I ever had.

M. Bonin
London EC2

Yes, I'm almost certain that's the same bloke I went out with. I slept with him on two occasions. The first time he only lasted two seconds. The next time he tried thinking about a field full of rotten cabbages and his performance improved dramatically, lasting all of two and a half pumps.

Carol Pope
Maghull, Merseyside

If Desmond Morris is such an expert on 'body language' how come he's got such a ridiculous haircut and dresses like a child molester?

Tom Chatterton
London SE22

You know where to stick 'em

'Countdown' has got to be my favourite TV programme. But to make it more interesting, why doesn't Carol Vorderman keep the consonants up her fanny and the vowels up her arse. The contestants would then have to ask for a "cuntsonant" or a "bowel", and the show could be re-titled "Cuntdown".

James Rae
Glasgow

Vith regards to ze German town of 'Wank' vhich you found so amusing in your last issue. On a recent holiday een Eengland I stopped to take zis photo of ein highly amusing town name sign. You see, in my country ze vird 'Bolton' means 'shitty arsehole'.

Jurgen Muller
Munich, Germany

What a rip-off these 'press on towels' are. It takes at least a dozen of them just to dry my arms.

R. Blackett
Peterlee

Congratulations on your choice of eyecatching 'soaks through the page' purple ink in issue 67. Readers were able to enjoy cartoons twice, first when they read them, and then again when they turned the page over. Another technical improvement would be printing the comic on lavatory paper so that in future I could flush it straight down the toilet.

Diarmid Campbell
Cambridge (not the university)

I realise I have missed your Viz character look-a-like competition, but is there any chance of a late entry for this Malcolm from Modern Parents look-a-like. He's even got the teeth. Do I win £5?

Mike Davies
Wirral

L-plates for jail baits

It's all well and good the Government introducing exams and tests for school children, and making driving tests more difficult. But how about a sexual proficiency test for school leavers? I went to bed with a 16 year old girl the other week and quite frankly she didn't have a clue what she was doing. It's no wonder Britain is lagging so far behind countries like Holland and Taiwan when half the girls leaving school can't tell their tits from their arses.

R. Jones
Bingley

Hey diddle diddle

In issue 67, the item about the Moon, you claim that cows cannot jump over the Moon. What codswallop. I own six calves who are only three weeks old and already they can jump over the 100 foot oak tree in their field. I'm prepared to bet you or any of your so-called readers a tenner they'll be able to jump over the Moon by the time they're fully grown.

Mrs J. Mills
Clearview Farm, Horam

So, Madonna has been voted the Least Sexy Woman in the world by the astute readers of Smash Hits magazine. Well, that's good news for the likes of Clare Short MP. I may not read Smash Hits, but I certainly know which one I'd rather have licking my bell end.

D. Lombard
Colchester

How about this for an unusual picture request. I challenge you to find a picture of Gloria Hunniford grinning broadly as she stabs a Zulu warrior with a spear!

T. Cake
Breadbin

That was some challenge, Mr Cake. After searching high and low we eventually had to admit defeat. The best we could do was this shot of Gloria stabbing a Masai tribesman. You win fair and square, and the £100 prize money is on its way to you.

I have been driving for over twenty years, and have never indicated either left or right in all that time. Why should I? It's nobody else's business where I'm going. I don't care where the person in front of me is going. He could be going to Timbuktu for all I care. So why should I have to tell the bloke behind me where I'm heading. He can mind his own bloody business.

R. Heart
Reading

I enjoy watching pro-celebrity golf and tennis, but how about pro-celebrity boxing? I would gladly pay £25 to watch Jonathon King slug it out for ten rounds with Frank Bruno.

A. Anderson
Hull

The police seem to think it's alright to put cameras anywhere they please in order to take photographs of our cars. Fair enough. Then I'm sure they won't mind if we hide in a tree and take a few photographs of their wives getting undressed through the bedroom window.

A. Fellows
Aston

No Smokie without fire

I wish people would stop taking the piss out of Smokie. They are my favourite group, and better than any of the so-called 'super groups' such as the Rolling Stones. They are a really nice bunch of guys too. I should know, they used to live next door to me.

Alice Wright
Stoke

This lesbian disease seems to be spreading to all our TV soaps nowadays. Is this really the sort of thing we want our families to watch? The BBC should bring back Dirty Den. He'd give these lesbians a bloody good seeing to. That would sort them out.

D. Fireplace
Ipswich

If God is in all places at all times then that means he's constantly in Paul Raymond's Revue Bar in Soho. Perhaps these so-called 'Christian's' could explain what in the Devil's name he is doing there?

K. Green
London W11

I refer to Mr B. Mink's letter (issue 66) enquiring about the availability of large melting pots. I am presently involved in an equally ambitious project, as I hope to teach the entire world to sing in perfect harmony. Having achieved this I should then like to hold the entire population of 4 or 5 billion in my arms, and keep them company. The next stage of the project will be to build the world a home and furnish it with love. Do any of your readers know where I could purchase large quantities of apple trees and honey bees and snow white turtle doves?

A. N. Seeker
Greenwich

What'll yule be doing this Christmas?

I cannot decide whether to stay at home, visit my parents, or go across to the in-laws on Christmas Day. I wonder whether other readers have decided what they are doing this year?

D.B.
Bromley

CONFUSE shopkeepers by buying a sheet of wrapping paper and asking them to wrap it.

D. Treloar
Wandsworth

A SIMPLE pocket calculator placed alongside your television is a constant source of amusement. Watch your friends' faces as they try in vain to change the TV channel with it.

P. T.
Aigburth

A LENGTH of plastic drainpipe with a roller skate attached to each end makes an ideal 'car' for snakes.

G. Dorson
Skipton

TELEPHONE salesmen. Increase company profits by reversing the charges whenever you call a customer. Invariably they'll accept the call, thinking it may be a relative in distress.

A. F.
London

Hull gets red light for sex

HULL is set to become a 'sex free zone' in a special experiment being carried out by the Department of Health. During the experiment, the first of its kind in Britain, residents will be subjected to a total ban on sex. The 'no nookie' rule is due to come into effect on August 1st this year and will continue for an indefinite period. Leaflets are due to be distributed throughout the Hull area advising residents of the ban. Road signs will be erected on all approach roads warning motorists not to have sex in Hull, and posters will be displayed at railway and bus stations.

*Hull yesterday.
(Well, Bolton anyway.)*

ISOLATED

"Hull was chosen for purely geographical reasons", says Dr. Ian Morris, spokesman for the Department of Health and the man responsible for maintaining the bonking ban. "Its isolated position makes it ideal for carrying out a controlled experiment of this kind".

TALKS

Department of Health officials have already been involved in talks with the Humberside Police Authority over possible methods of implementing the ban. Among ideas being considered are sophisticated electronic 'black boxes' which would be placed on bedside tables. Couples would be required to insert a 'smart card' before having sex. The cards would be available from Post Offices, and anyone trying to buy one would be told that they couldn't.

SUCCESS

If the experiment proves to be a success Health officials hope to extend the ban to cover the whole of Britain. "It will be at least two years before we are in a position to make that decision, but hopefully a nationwide ban on sexual intercourse could be in place by as early as Spring 1997, said Dr. Morris.

MAKE cheap but effective baby rattles by gluing a lollipop stick to an empty matchbox, then filling it with ten woodlice.

Ms. G. M. Dowd
Wigan

FOR those who haven't got enough money for two weeks holiday, go for one week and don't go to bed.

Christopher 'Monty' Heading
Aged 8. Nottingham

FOIL pick pockets by placing a freshly toasted 'Pop Tart' in each pocket. Would-be thieves will quickly rupture the fragile pastry and receive nasty finger burns from the steaming hot jam inside.

P. Turner
Liverpool L17

AVOID 'red eye' when taking flash photographs by sticking a small piece of black tape over the flash bulb on the front of your camera.

D. Burton
Felling

AVOID burns from a hot iron by placing the garment over a hot ring on the electric cooker, and then rubbing it with a cold iron.

M. T.
Greenwich

STEAL money from flat-mates by borrowing £5 then moving to Fife. (If you live in Fife, move to South Fife).

Anon.
Fife

SET UP a Haagen Das ice cream franchise next door to your local Weight Watchers clinic. Give away freebies to slim people and watch the fat fuckers squirm.

D. R.
Croydon

'I will not eat snakes'

Geordie hard man actor, writer, director and producer Jimmy Nail was close to tears yesterday as he told a hushed press gathering, "I would never eat snakes."

SCARED

However, Nail, who shot to stardom as a German bricklayer in TV's 'Spender', denied being scared of the reptiles. "I'm not scared of them. I just wouldn't eat them," he told reporters.

"I certainly wouldn't allow my kids to keep them as pets," he added, when pressed on the subject. "I wouldn't have them in the house. But not because I'm scared of them. Just because they wouldn't make very good pets."

YOBS!
Windsor's night of shame

Prince Charles - Fight on dance floor

Members of the Royal Family have been carpeted by the Queen after a celebration pub crawl ended in mayhem and violence in a boozy nightclub brawl.

Diners at the posh Muchos Millionaires Nitespot and Mexican diner in Windsor, Berks. were stunned when members of the Royal Family gatecrashed a private function and demanded booze. A heated argument broke out between the Duke of Edinburgh and one diner, and the guest later claimed he was punched in the face by the Queen Mother.

DESTRUCTION

The rowdy Royals left a trail of destruction in their wake as the blue-blooded boozers painted the town red. It is believed they were celebrating a successful day's horse racing. Trouble flared in several pubs and the Royal party were refused drink in at least one town centre bar.

Bender ends in Royals wreck

Things got out of hand when staff at the Blue Monkey refused them service. As landlord Malcolm Howard explains.

SPIRITS

"They came in at about 7pm and were in high spirits. I'd say they were merry, but certainly not causing any bother. Prince Charles signed a few autographs for the locals, and the Duke of Edinburgh was playing pool. But it was 'happy hour' and treble spirits only cost a pound before 8pm. They were knocking them back like there was no tomorrow. By 7.30 I decided they'd had enough, and I asked them if they would leave. Some of my regulars were being offended by the strong language they were using".

BEERS

"Prince Charles ignored me and asked for another round of trebles. His voice was

Queen Mother punched diner in face after row erupted over 'ginger top' insult

slurred and his manner was aggressive. He took out a five pound note and pointed at the Queen. "Do you know who that it is?" he said. "That's my f***ing mum that is". I told him he'd had enough, and that he should leave. Eventually they went, although we later discovered six pool balls were missing and there was urine in one of the pockets of the table".

WINES

The group of Royal yobs later made their way to the nightclub where the doorman Dave Watson recognised them. "We had a private function on that night but we have a policy of letting Royals in because they're good for business, and you don't expect their sort to cause trouble". Dave recognised at least five Royals as the party rolled up the street, singing and carrying on. "Prince Charles, the Duke of Edinburgh, Princess Margaret and the Duke and

Duchess of Kent and a couple of others turned up just after pub closing time", he told us.

"I told them if they calmed down they could come inside. But they'd only been in the place twenty minutes when I was called to break up a fight on the dance floor involving Prince Charles."

According to one eye witness Charles had been talking to a group of girls when a scuffle broke out. Tina Harper had been sitting with friends when the heir to the throne approached them. "He was really obnoxious, walking from girl to girl and asking if they know who he was? He

Prince Philip - offered £50 to see wife's tits.

really seemed to fancy himself. He grabbed one girl by

BY OUR ROYAL CORRESPONDENTS
THE ALAN RODGERS CONNECTION

the arm and tried to kiss her, but her boyfriend stepped in and a couple of punches were thrown. Charles fell, knocking over several drinks. I don't think any of the punches made contact, he was just so drunk he couldn't stand up".

PANTIES

Worse was to follow when the Duke of Edinburgh climbed onto a table and offered £100 to any girl who would strip off down to her panties. "We were totally disgusted. They all thought it was hilarious, but no-one else did. It's not the sort of behaviour you expect from members of the Royal Family", said Tina.

BRAS

Meanwhile, barman Brian Campbell was attempting to prevent further trouble. "Prince Philip had got into a row with a group of diners in the restaurant. He had been offering one gentleman fifty pounds to see his wife's tits. He was completely over the top. He started calling the bloke a 'carrot topped bastard'. The poor guy had ginger hair and was trying to keep his cool but eventually something snapped and the geezer got up and had a go. You couldn't blame him. Next thing I knew the Queen Mother had jumped in and all hell broke loose".

MRS. CAT the NURSE

Queen Mum - punched diner in face

Tits bounce back

Large ones set for comedy come-back

By our Tits Correspondent
LEE HARVEY OSWALD

The showbiz world is today buzzing with the news that big tits are set to be funny again.

For many years large breasts were considered extremely funny, reaching a peak of popularity in the mid seventies. But comedy tastes changed and while other comedy items like sausages and cheese remained, by the end of the decade big busts were no longer considered amusing by the British public. But now the tables have turned, and experts believe ample bosoms could be set for and imminent comedy come-back.

KISS

"Big tits are definitely funny" one TV insider told us yesterday. "For years they have been the kiss of death, but now people are starting to take notice of them again, and I think they are set to be hilarious over the next few years".

STRYPER

One positive sign that things are looking up for big tits was the announcement that Barbara Windsor is set to appear in the BBC soap EastEnders. Saucy star of the Carry On films, Barbara's bosoms were among the biggest comedy tits of the seventies. And in November she is due to hit the screens as the Mitchell twins' TV mother.

An official EastEnders spokesman refused to be drawn on the size of Barbara Windsor's tits. "We're delighted Barbara has joined the cast. She's a very talented and popular actress and we're sure her character will be a hit with the viewers", he said.

WIZARD

However one high ranking insider confirmed that Barbara's big tits are being seen as a secret weapon in the battle for viewers. "Obviously Barbara has been recruited first and foremost for her talent as an actress", he told us. "But having said that, the

Babs - Big boobs

big tits are there, and I'd be a liar if I said we won't be using them for comedy effect whenever we can".

Other people with big tits include Dolly Parten, Dawn French, Kate Bush and Raquel Welsh.

A girl with big tits in the seventies

...ing restaurant

Police were called but by the time they arrived the Royal party had left, leaving an estimated £5,000 worth of damage to fixtures and fittings in the club. One guest, a

Duke of Edinburgh offered girls £100 to strip

man in his late thirties, needed hospital treatment for a broken nose. Club owner Michael Fellows says that the Royals have since offered to pay for the damage. "Charles offered to pay for everything on condition we kept the

whole thing quiet. But I refused. He even offered to buy me a new restaurant. But this isn't about money. I think its only right people should know what their future King and his family get up to".

GIRDLES

A Buckingham Palace spokesman yesterday confirmed that the Queen would be disciplining members of the Royal Family over the incident, although no names were mentioned. In the past fines of up to £2,000 have been levied for breaches of etiquette, and bringing the Royals into disrepute. A spokesman for the police said that so far charges had not been brought against the Queen Mother, although he confirms that the elderly Royal had been questioned by officers investigating an alleged assault.

Colin CONTROVERSIAL
The man who dares SAY IT

Roy Castle brave? Rubbish

How many times in these last few weeks have we been told what a brave man Roy Castle was? What on earth was brave about dying of lung cancer? As far as I was aware he didn't have any choice.

It is brave men like Walt Disney, Yul Bryner and Nat 'King' Cole, men who

chose to smoke, and in so doing gave their lives, that we should admire.

We should pay tribute to *their* bravery, and not the cowardly actions of a man who throughout his life didn't have the guts to puff on a single cigarette.

Her Royal Highness the QUEER Mother

Everyone heaps praise on the Queen Mum. They talk about her lovely smile, her radiant looks, her wonderful hats. I often wonder whether I'm looking at the same woman.

Has no-one noticed what awful teeth she's got?

All the other female Royals; the Queen, Princess Anne, and even Fergie, have all

got fellas. But not the Queen Mother. Perhaps there's something we haven't been told.

We all know she's a fan of horse racing. Well I'd say it was a good *each way bet* that this nag's queer!

They must have said something

Let's face it, those Jews in the war must have said something pretty nasty to Hitler. After all, even a Nazi would have to be bloody annoyed to murder six million people.

We obviously don't know the full story. So let's not jump to any conclusions until we get all the facts.

There. I've said it.

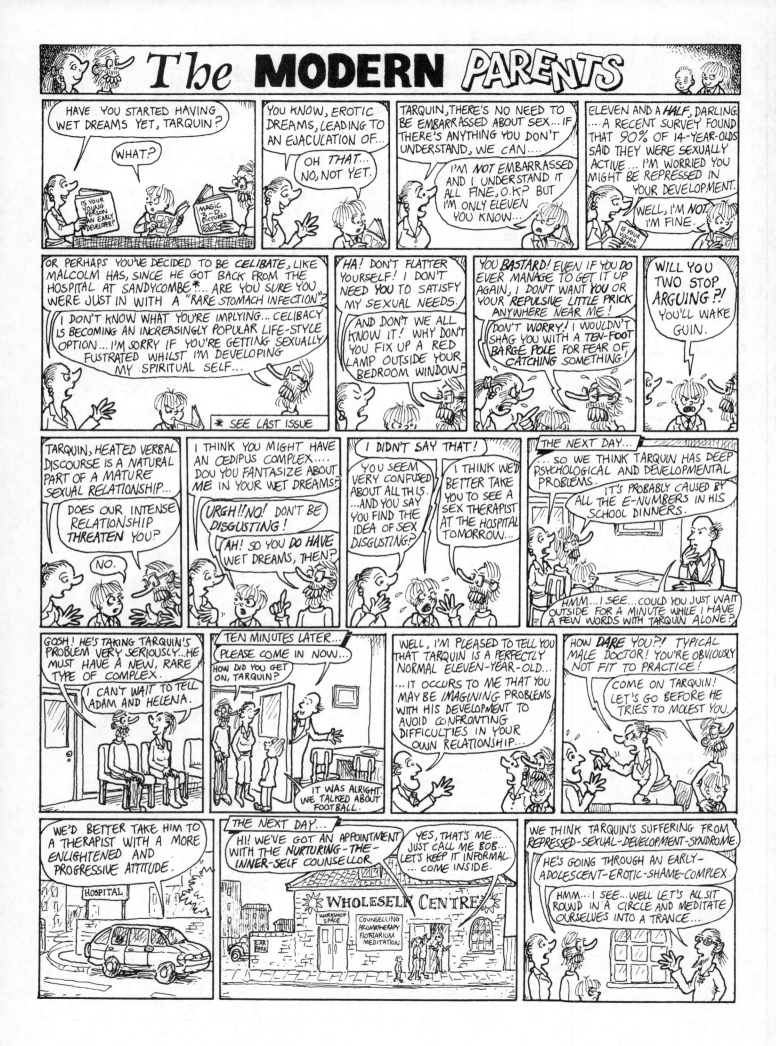

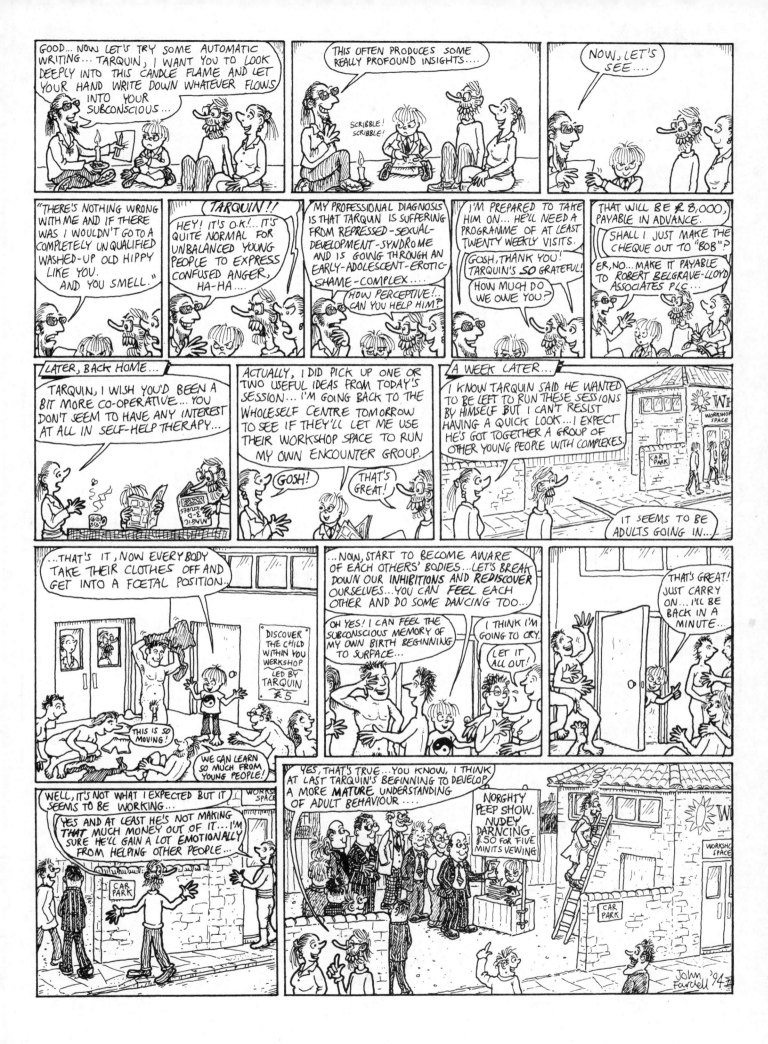

It's time these quacks piped down

Toast to the brave

AS WE approach Christmas I believe the time is right to pay tribute to a group of people whose bravery is so often overlooked. Drink drivers. So often a target for the knockers and the boo boys, here is a group of single-minded men and women who are prepared to risk imprisonment, injury or even death for something in which they believe. A simple thing called drinking and driving.

I propose a toast to these brave men and women. And afterwards I shall be driving home.

There's been a lot of talk about how smoking killed Roy Castle. What a load of nonsense. Smoking is good for you. Ask any doctor.

I wish these scaremongers would pipe down. They're the same nutcases who tell us to swing our heads from side to side every time we wish to cross the road, and that we mustn't turn right on motorways.

INTENTION

Well I've got news for them. I'll drive in any direction I want to drive. And I have every intention of stopping occasionally to have a cigarette.

How long must the killers carry the can?

The I.R.A. have been given a pretty rough ride by certain sections of the media over the last few years.

They have been made scapegoats for the murders and bombings which they have committed.

It's easy to lay blame for appalling terrorist crimes at the door of those who carried them out. We could condemn these killings until the cows come home, and further. But aren't we closing the barn door after the horse has already been bolted? Isn't it about time we considered putting the cart *before* the horse, instead of counting chickens that have already been layed?

Let's call a spade a kettle. Some things are easier said than done. Unfortunately, murder is one of them.

HOORAY FOR HOLLYWOOD

A lot has been written about the bizarre marriage of Michael Jackson to Elvis Presley. It's pure Hollywood, isn't it. It couldn't happen anywhere else.

The cheap talk has been about a marriage of convenience, a cover-up aimed at glossing over Jackson's sexual indiscretions with kids, monkeys and dwarfs. Such garbage doesn't bear repeating.

Millions

Michael Jackson's music has brought joy to millions. And to many Elvis remains the King, long after his tragic slaying. I have nothing but contempt for the man who shot Elvis, and my heart goes out to the children and monkeys.

But isn't it time we let bygones be bygones, and allowed this tragic couple to live the remainder of their all too short lives in peace?

Michael Jackson in 1972 yesterday.

LET'S GIVE THESE KILLERS A BREAK

There's been a lot of cheap criticism levelled at child murderers in certain newspapers lately. These people are an easy target for the knockers. But I think we should give them their fair dues.

Murderers

They provide stories for the press and work for the police. And in this day and age that's not bad going.

Why not give the child murderers and sex fiends a break, and try having a go at a smaller target for a change, like the young children on whom they prey. Invariably these children are no angels themselves.

SILENCE OF THE SIXTIES BEAT GROUPS

Surviving stars of the sixties beat era were today remaining tight lipped over allegations that top recording artists of the day experimented with gruesome act of cannibalism.

The stories, which originate from an unknown source, claim the top acts of the era got together for regular flesh eating orgies, staying up late at night, drinking and eating dismembered human bodies.

IDOLS

Their victims were teenage fans who innocently followed the groups back to hotels in search of autographs. Minders would invite selected girls to join their idols in a hotel bedroom where they would be murdered by the stars who would then greedily feast on their flesh.

LIARS

Observers fear that up to two hundred 'missing persons' who disappeared during the sixties and remain unaccounted for may have been killed in this way by groups such as Brian Poole and the Tremeloes. The Tremeloes enjoyed a string of hits in the early sixties, topping the chart in September 1963 with 'Do You Love Me'.

GRAHAMS

One mother whose daughter has not disappeared yesterday sympathised with the parents of children possibly murdered by the sixties beat groups. "The longer this goes on the more these people

Stars tight lipped over cannibal claims

suffer", she told us. "It's the not knowing which is the most painful thing. If only these people would come forward and tell the truth, and put an end to this suffering".

JOELS

Gerry Marsden, who with his beat combo The Pacemakers set Merseyside dance floors alight thirty years ago, refused to discuss the fate of

Gerry & the Pacemakers. No comment on flesh eating orgy allegations.

innocent teenage fans whose bodies may have been eaten alive in stomach churning ritualistic orgies of sexual violence. Gerry and the Pacemakers were of course best known for the Liverpool anthem 'Ferry Across The Mersey', one of seven top twenty hits the group enjoyed. The Merseybeats were another successful male vocal/instrumental group of the era whose impressive chart record is now left

clouded by these most shocking of allegations.

CRYSTALS

The sixties beat explosion focused strongly on Merseyside with The Beatles enormous success paving the way for a host of other fresh faced local groups. There is however no evidence to suggest that The Beatles themselves were ever involved in acts of cannibalism.

A spokesman for an electrical shop near the Merseyside home of Gerry Marsden yesterday denied having supplied the veteran singer with any fridges big enough to keep a human head in. "I didn't know he lived round here", he told us. "I certainly don't recall selling him a fridge". If kept refrigerated the flesh from a human head could remain edible for two to three days.

MR. MOLE the OPTICIAN

D.I.V.O.R.C.E. spells JACKPOT!

Breaking up is hard to do but it might just be worth it for *forty million smackers*

The break-up of any marriage is a tragedy for all concerned. And our heart-felt sympathies go out to Phil and Jill Collins at this difficult time.

The fact that Phil is now free to play the field and pull a fantastic fat titted young bird is precious little consolation for the heartache and pain that the millionaire singer has endured. And for Phil's wife Jill a cool **£40 million** slice of the old man's action can never begin to replace what she has lost. Although it could come in pretty handy.

JUMBO

Jill's jumbo pay-off will send cash registers ringing all over showbusiness, with eager wives eying up bank balances with a view to divorce. So just how easy would it be for the wives of the stars to get their hands on their hubbies' assets? We asked our special undercover reporter **Mandy Morrisroe** to find out by calling the stars and pre-tending to be their wives. Mischievous Mandy then demanded divorce, and began haggling. Here's how she got on.

DUMBO

PAUL McCARTNEY has more loot stashed away than most other pop stars put together. Over **£200 MILLION** at the last count. And without Linda, a linchpin in his band Wings, Paul would be penniless. So we figured his wife was worth £150 million.
"Hello. Is that you Paul? It's me, your wife Linda McCartney", said our girl Mandy, holding a hand-kerchief over the phone. "Pardon?" replied Paul.

NELLIE

"Our marriage… it isn't working, and I want a divorce", said Mandy. There was a silence on the end of the line.
"I want £150 million, in cash", she continued.
But Paul is a shrewd bus-inessman, and rather than cave in to our demands, he decided to put the phone down.

Former Bond Moore

was determined the multi-millionaire star would pay dearly to dump his real life wife Luisa. This time Mandy dropped Moore a line at his agent's office, cleverly dis-guising her handwriting as his wife's.

'Dear Roger. Things are not working out between us. I think a divorce would be best and I will settle for £5 million. Love, Luisa'.

BABAR

Three days after posting the letter Mandy had heard nothing so she wrote again,

Sexy Mandy chats to a star

Viz girl Mandy goes *undercover* with the stars

this time demanding only £1 million, and telling Roger he could see the kids at week-ends. But still no reply. The former Bond was obviously *shaken but not stirred* by her demands.

LITTLE BLUE

Finally, Mandy decided to call up Britain's top TV celebrity **NOEL EDMUNDS** and take the money-grabbing so-and-so for every penny he had.

"Hello Noel. Gill here. I'm afraid our marriage is over. Let's talk money", she said. "I want the lot".
"Is this some sort of a wind up?" Edmunds replied. "Who is that? Don't tell me, you're recording this aren't you!"
"No, I'm not", replied our undercover girl.
"Well fuck off then", said Edmunds.

As James Bond actor **ROGER MOORE** often cast beautiful women by the wayside. But our Mandy

EXCLUSIVE

No jacket required for millionaire Phil seen on one of his last dates with wife Jill.

Four inch 'sex monkeys' wanked in my tea - says Sting

POP singer Sting shocked guests at a four star hotel by claiming that pint sized monkeys had masturbated into tea delivered to his room by hotel staff.

A fellow guest overheard the star's conversation with staff at the posh Sandy Bay hotel near Toronto. "Sting claimed that sex monkeys, less than four inches tall, had got into his room through a gap in the window frame", the guest told us.

SUMMONED

Eventually hotel manag-er Mark Lavender was summoned to settle the dispute. He accompa-nied Sting to the room but could find no evi-dence of sex monkeys.

"There was a slight ingress of water around the aluminium window frame, but this had occurred over a period of time", he told National Enquirer magazine. "There was absolutley no way a monkey, no matter how small, could have entered the room at that point."

REFUSED

Yesterday a hotel spoke-sman refused to say whether Sting had suc-cessfully negotiated a reduction in his bill over

Mr Sting last Thursday

the matter. "I am not at liberty to discuss any individual's bill. You will have to take the matter up with Mr Sting him-self", we were told. Sting's best friend, for-mer Mastermind cham-pion Fred Housego was last night unavailable for comment.

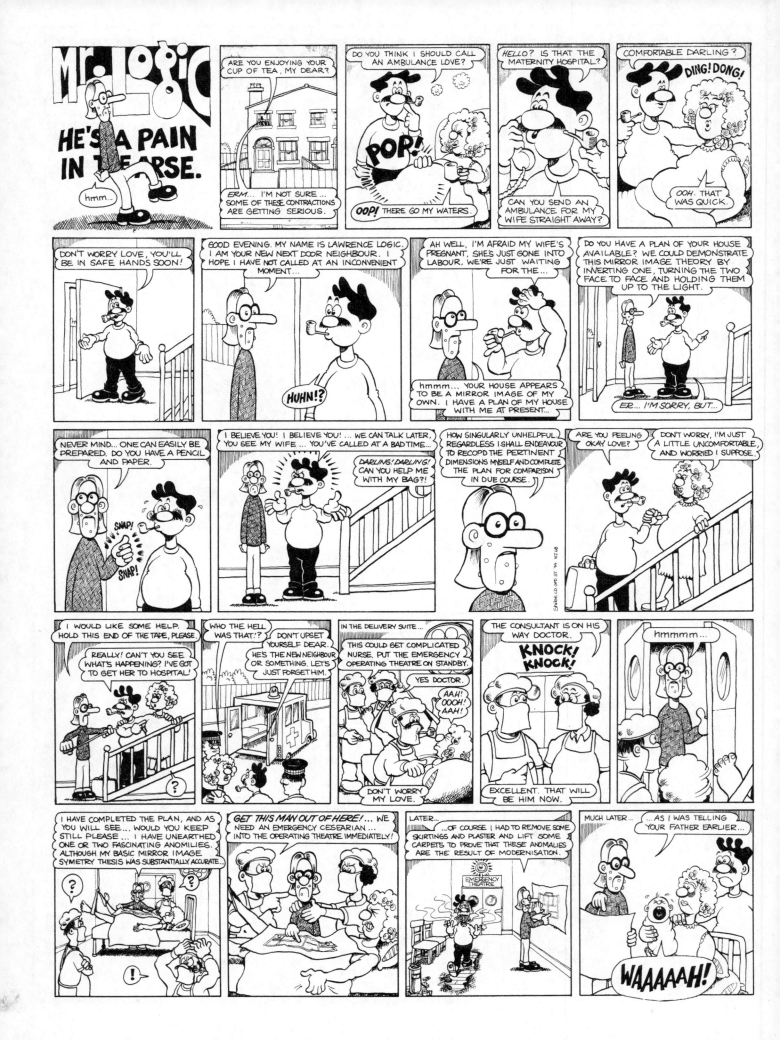

FANTASY EX-FOOTBALLER PUB MANAGEMENT

The most realistic fantasy football game yet

We've all dreamt of being a Premier League manager and picking a side to win the title. But have you ever imagined being an overweight ex-footballer managing a pub? Well now's your chance to do just that with our fantastic fantasy game that combines the thrills and spills of Premier League soccer with the action and excitement of pub management.

The aim of the game is for you, the landlord, to put on as much weight as you can in the course of a season by eating and drinking as much of your stock as you can. Your success will depend entirely upon the real-life performances of your dream team of Premiership players.

DREAM

First, you must select your dream team to help you run the pub from the squad of Pemiership players below. Instead of a transfer market value for each player we have given the hourly rate that you would have to pay them to work in your pub. Your total staff budget is £60 an hour, so you must pick a team whose hourly wages do not exceed £60.

FISH

The scoring system is simple. Instead of points you accumulate *calories* as you pile on the pounds throughout the season. For every Premiership goal scored by one of your players, a customer who recognises you from your playing days buys you three pints of beer and a packet of peanuts. If a player scores a hat trick you get nine points, plus a treble whisky and two packets of nuts. For every 'assist' credited to one of your players you nip behind the bar and pull yourself one pint, and grab a packet of crisps. Every time your

goalkeeper keeps a clean sheet you have a lock-in and get through ten pints, six whiskies and three packets of peanuts.

T-SHIRT

Every Saturday add up the number of Premiership points won by the eleven clubs to which your players belong. For each point you pull yourself a pint to celebrate, every evening for a week. So multiply the points total by 7 to get your points to pints total for the week. Every week calculate your net weight gain by converting your fantasy food and drink intake into calories using this table.

Pint of beer
250 calories
Packet of salted nuts
500 calories
Whisky per measure
150 calories
Packet of crisps
150 calories

For the purposes of this Fantasy Ex-Footballer Pub Management game, for every 8,000 calories you accumulate you gain 1 pound in weight.

WET WET

To play the game simply complete the form below, naming your pub and your team of players/bar staff. Unfortunately we do not have a computer so it will be necessary for you to calculate your own results

each week and notify us by post. An updated Fantasy Ex-Footballer Pub Management league table will appear in each issue. The winner will be the landlord who has put on the most weight by the end of the

season, and he will win our first prize: An executive box for life at the Premiership club of his choice, £10 million to spend on footballers, a bucket of diamonds and a gold mine.

Ryan Giggs

The Tankerville Arms

Selecting your team

The Premiership players listed here are in 5 categories: Glass Collectors (GC), Cellar Men (CM), Cleaners (CL), Bar Staff (BS) and Bouncers (BO). Your team must be made up of 1 x GC, 2 x CM, 2 x CL, 4 x BS and 2 x BO. The initials after each player's name and club indicate his position: Goalkeeper (GK), Full back (FB), Centre back (CB), Midfield (MF) and Striker (ST).

When selecting glass collector (GC) it is not always advisable to choose a goalkeeper (GK). No matter how safe his hands may seem, for every Premiership goal he concedes he will drop 4 pint pots.

When choosing bar staff (BS) avoid strikers (ST). If a striker misses a penalty then your till will be out £10 at the end of the evening.

And try not to choose defenders (FB and CB) as cellar men (CM). Every time they concede a goal they allow a keg of lager to run out. And if a defender cellar man (FBCBCM) concedes a penalty then the bitter has gone off and you loose half a keg. If you select a goalkeeper as cellar man (GKCM) and he concedes a goal then he forgets to clean the lines after changing the Guinness over.

A wise choice as bouncer (BO) would be a striker (ST), but try to avoid hot-headed characters like Cantona. For if he gets booked in the Premiership he punches a customer in the face and the police are called. A red card and he is charged with causing grievous bodily harm, convicted and sentenced to 6 months communty service.

Eric Cantona

Name of pub ....

Glass Collector 1 ....

Cellar Men 2 .... 3 ....

Cleaners 5 .... 6 ....

Bar Staff 4 .... 7 ....

8 .... 11 ....

Bouncers 9 .... 10 ....

Your name .... Address ....

....

I am over 18 and have been interested in football for at least two weeks.

Signed ....

The Red Lion

The Black Bull

Glass Collectors		Cellar Men		Cleaners		Bar Staff		Bouncers	
Ryan Giggs (Man Utd) MF ST	£8.75 per hour	Tim Flowers (Blackburn) GK	£8.50 per hour	Ruel Fox (Newcastle) MF	£8.00 per hour	Matt le Tissier (So'ton) ST	£8.00 per hour	Phil Babb (Liverpool) CB	£8.00 per hour
Jurgen Kinsman (Spurs) ST	£8.75 per hour	Neil Ruddock (Liverpool) CB	£7.00 per hour	Tony Adams (Arsenal) CB	£7.50 per hour	Les Ferdinand (QPR) ST	£7.50 per hour	Eric Cantona (Man Utd) ST	£8.00 per hour
John Barnes (Liverpool) MF	£6.25 per hour	Gary Pallister (Man Utd) CB	£6.50 per hour	Stan Collymore (Forest) ST	£7.50 per hour	David Seaman (Arsenal) GK	£7.30 per hour	Jan Molby (Liverpool) MFK	£7.25 per hour
Robert Lee (Newcastle) MF	£6.00 per hour	Vinny Samways (Spurs) MF	£5.50 per hour	Dennis Wise (Chelsea) MF	£6.80 per hour	Gavin Peacock (Chelsea) MF ST	£6.45 per hour	Chris Waddle (Sheff Wed) MF	£6.85 per hour
Martin Allen (West Ham) MF	£5.00 per hour	Dean Saunders (Villa) ST	£5.25 per hour	Andre Kanchelskis (Man Utd) MF	£6.80 per hour	Niall Quinn (Man City) ST	£4.25 per hour	Barry Venison (Newcastle) CB FB	£6.50 per hour
David James (Liverpool) GK	£4.25 per hour	Tony Cottee (West Ham) ST	£4.25 per hour	Roy Wegerle (Coventry) ST	£5.75 per hour	David Speedie (Leicester) ST	£3.85 per hour	Ian Dowie (So'ton) ST	£5.75 per hour
Michael Vonk (Man City) CB	£3.75 per hour	Rod Wallace (Leeds) ST	£3.80 per hour	Darren Anderton (Spurs) MF	£5.25 per hour	Chris Bart-Williams (Sheff Wed) MF	£3.50 per hour	Dennis Urwin (Man Utd) FB	£4.80 per hour
Mark Wright (Liverpool) CB	£3.50 per hour	Kevin Scott (Spurs) ST	£2.80 per hour	John Fashanu (Villa) ST	£3.80 per hour	Scott Gemmill (Forest) MF	£2.80 per hour	Steve Howey (Newcastle) CB	£4.25 per hour
Stuart Ripley (Blackburn) MF	£2.85 per hour	Gary Penrice (QPR) ST	£2.00 per hour	Steve McManaman (Liverpool) MFT	£3.25 per hour	Nigel Winterburn (Arsenal) FB	£2.25 per hour	Chris Fairclough (Leeds) CB	£3.25 per hour
George Ndah (Crystal Palace) MF	£2.25 per hour	Lee Chapman (West Ham) ST	£1.25 per hour	Anders Limpar (Everton) MF	£2.00 per hour	Scott Minto (Chelsea) FB	£2.20 per hour	Garry Mabbutt (Spurs) CB	£2.85 per hour

Richard Littlecock

LITTLE COCK   BIG OPINION

Animal rights? Animal WRONGS!

Animal rights activists get under my collar. These so-called 'vegetarians' refuse to eat meat on the grounds that animals suffer. *Animals* suffer?

I'll tell you who suffers. People like **ME** suffer having to listen to this minority of nutcases trotting out their ill-conceived advice to the vast majority of sensible meat-eating folk. First of all, let's get some facts straight.

Facts

Fact No. 1. Animals **CANNOT** suffer pain. It simply isn't possible. You'd have more chance of hurting a cauliflower. Animals, like sheep, dogs and monkeys, do not have brains. They live like flowers, sucking water up from the ground, and eating sunshine. Kick them, poke them, bite them. Rest assured they will feel no pain. They may jump, or make a noise, but so do trees. That proves nothing.

Fact No. 2. Man **CANNOT** survive by eating vegetables. If you try to survive on vegetables alone, you will die. Simple as that. You might just as well try living on a diet of popcorn.

Fact No. 3. Eggs do **NOT** come from hens.

They are the facts. *Now, would the long-haired idiots who persist in screaming "murder" every time someone kills a pig please shut up while I have a bacon sandwich.* Thank you.

It's time to blow our own trumpets

The late great Roy Castle will be sadly missed.

In fact he will be missed a damn sight more than most of us realise. He was brave, he was funny, he was kind, he was caring. But more than all those things Roy Castle could *play the trumpet.*

Britain needs men who can play the trumpet. In an age where wealth has become all important, where respect for others is sadly lacking, where soap operas mean more to us than real life, now more than ever before we need to play the trumpet.

Trumpets

In the past trumpet players were two a penny. Kenny Ball. Young men joined the army to fight, and to play the trumpet. Night clubs were packed with people dancing, and playing the trumpet. Trumpet factories worked overtime as Britain rode the crest of a musical wave. But now that wave has broken. And among the frothy swirls of salt water which lap at our feet, licking the sand from between our toes, there is no longer the sound of trumpets.

Britain *needs* trumpet players. We owe it to *ourselves* to *learn* the trumpet. For without trumpet players the sound of the trumpet will die. Like the late Roy Castle.

King's Crossed wires

Stunned train travellers stood in silence as they listened to their future King having oral sex over a passenger announcement system yesterday.

Commuters at Kings Cross awaiting news of cancellations or delays couldn't believe their ears when instead they heard the unmistakable sound of Prince Charles having oral sex with his mistress Camilla Parker-Bowles.

"It was unbelievable", said one passenger. "It's not the behaviour you'd expect from a future King", he added.

TRAIN

Charles' cock-up occurred after his Royal train broke down and he was offered the use of a room at the station until it was mended. According to an insider the passionate Prince smuggled his old flame into the room in a laundry basket. "The minute heads were turned she popped out and the pair of them got straight down to business", we were told.

"An incident did occur at Kings Cross station involving Prince Charles and Camilla Parker-Bowles", said a brief official statement released by British Rail yesterday. "Unfortunately Prince Charles switched a microphone on by

A red faced Camilla leaving Kings Cross

mistake whilst having oral sex with Camilla Parker-Bowles on an office desk" it added.

"I don't think he should be King any more", said one dithering old lady we spoke to yesterday. Do **YOU** think Charles is fit to be King after having oral sex at Kings Cross station? Why not call us and tell us what YOU think.

For **YES** – Ring
(091) 2 12 12 13

For **NO** – Ring
(091) 2 121 21 3

Your calls will be charged at normal BT rates.

Commuters get an earful of Charles's mouthfull

MR. DOG the POLICEMAN

Tree profits up

Trees have announced a pre-tax profit of £265 million for the last fiscal year. The figure is almost double last year's profit and as a result wood prices soared on the markets yesterday.

Shelves were up 40p to £2.90 and for the first time ever broom handles were changing hands for £4.00 each.

Meanwhile, there was bad news for sparrows who announced a record loss of over £10 million. Sparrows have been badly hit by an increase in the weather lately, however one leading city analyst predicted a slow recovery. "All the early signs are that sparrows will rebuild and consolidate over the coming months. In 1994 sparrows look an attractive proposition to foreign investors, compared to uncertainty in other sectors such as thatched roofs and static electricity. I can see a gradual recovery taking shape over the next six to twelve months".

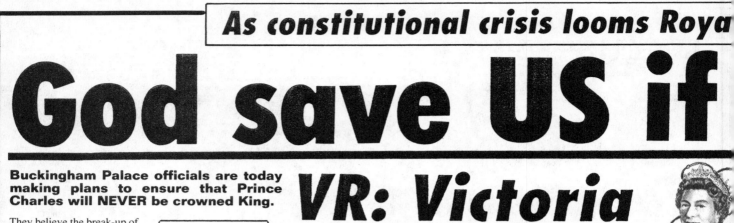

God save US if

Buckingham Palace officials are today making plans to ensure that Prince Charles will NEVER be crowned King.

They believe the break-up of the marriage between the Prince and Princess of Wales will create a constitutional crisis should Charles ever take the throne. For Dirty Di is thought to have her eyes on the Crown Jewels, and will demand to be Queen even if the couple divorce. And there is added concern over the fact that Charles is thought to be losing his marbles.

CLOGS

Backstage at the Palace Royal chiefs have been frantically making plans to prevent big-eared Charles taking the hot seat should his mother pop her Royal clogs. Palace insiders have confirmed that they are considering several possible alternatives, one of which could involve a surprise comeback for Queen Victoria.

MORRISES

Victoria, Britain's most popular Royal to date, is known to be 'not amused' by the current goings on at the Palace. Since retiring to Eastbourne in the fifties she has remained out of the limelight. But she may be asked to return in a possible 'caretaker Queen' capacity should the present Monarch throw a seven.

SQUARES

"Her frumpy Royal image is just what's required to take the steam out of the situation at present", one insider told us. "Despite her age she could probably cope with the media quite well, and I'm sure she'd accept the job, providing it was only on a temporary basis".

HEP CATS

A return to the throne so long after her reign officially ended at the turn of the century would be unusual, but as Royal pundits point out, there have been precedents. In 1979 former West Ham manager Ron Greenwood came out of retirement to act as caretaker manager to the England team after Don Revie had quit the post to

By the late DAVID NIXON

work abroad in Saudi Arabia. And Malcom Allison made stop-gap appearances at both Manchester City and Crystal Palace to see his old clubs through crisis periods.

TOP CATS

One advantage of a return for Queen Vic would be that old money and stamps, already featuring her head, could simply be re-used, saving a fortune in new designs. John Major is thought to support the idea, as Victoria's return would guarantee a return to Victorian values, something which the present government strongly favours.

VR: Victoria to Return?

Are these the monarchies of the future? Queen Victoria (left) could be set for surprise comeback. Or will the Queen be a Dalek?

Palace plan to put her 'on ice'

But another option thought to be favoured by the Royal Family is to freeze the Queen in a 'Walt Disney' style fridge. By this method the Queen's death could be postponed indefinitely, and neither Charles or Di could get their hands on the throne. Despite dying of lung cancer in 1967, Walt Disney is still able to mastermind his multi-billion dollar cartoon empire from his $5 million detached Hollywood fridge freezer.

TOP HATS

Using the same technology the Queen could simply be frozen and kept alive forever inside the Tower of London. Although unable to say or do anything, it is thought she would never-the-less be able to fulfil her Royal duties, and pre-recorded speeches could be shown on Christmas Day.

BOWLERS

However, a third option, believed to be favoured by the Queen herself, is by far

the more likely to get the go ahead. Royal physicians are believed to have opened talks with BBC 'Dr Who' creator Terry Nation, if he's

A Dalek yesterday (left) and Dr Who tomorrow (right).

'Dalek' option is being considered

still alive, with a view to converting the existing Queen into a 'Dalek' style half humanoid, half robot.

Royal chiefs were particularly impressed with the performance of the Dalek's leader 'Davros' in the BBC television series.

FIELDERS

Davros, creator of the Daleks, was half humanoid, having

created a Dalek style body for himself after suffering radiation injuries in a war between the Kaleds and the Tharls, on the planet Skaros. He went on to create the army of robotic monsters known as the Daleks, who in time became arch enemies of Dr Who.

WICKIES

Converting the Queen to half Dalek would be a relatively straightforward operation. A Dalek base would be required in which she would sit, and pipes and tubes would then be attached to her head. She would move around and talk by operating switches on a small control panel in front of her. However, the potential problems would be limitless, as one former Dr Who told us.

BATSMAN

William Hartnell was the first television Doctor, and came face to face with the Daleks in black and white during the early sixties. Although now dead, he recalls only too well his great robotic adversaries. "I'd be very weary of making the Queen into a Dalek", he told us, speaking from his £200,000 Essex grave. "She would inevitably take on

hiefs pray...

Queen croaks

Scarey monarchs. A hissing Martian Ice Warrior (above) and a terrifying Sea Devil (below) complete with his deadly underwater torch.

many Dalek characteristics, and that is where the problems would begin".

ROBSIN

"Daleks are cruel and emotionless, and have very unpleasant voices. In times of stress they tend to repeat themselves, over and over again, at a steadily increasing pitch, often spinning around in a frenzy during moments of high excitement. Whether this behaviour would be becoming of a monarch on a state occasion must be open to question".

Experts agree that with several minor alterations a standard Dalek shell could easily be adapted to suit a Royal role. "One obvious change could be replacing the Dalek's exterminator gun with a sword, so that the Queen could Knight people. And instead of a sucker, a small hand could be added, for waving", said one source yesterday.

Palace officials face monster decision

"Exterminate! Exterminate!" So said the Daleks in their numerous TV battles with Dr Who. But of all the Doctor's adversaries, is a Dalek the most suited to becoming our future Queen? Here we take a brief look at a few other Dr Who monsters, and assess their suitability to the greatest roll of all, that of Queen of England.

The Cybermen were silver robotic monsters with Hoover pipes down their arms and silver practice golf balls on their shoulders. Frozen in tombs on the planet Telos, they were briefly revived by a power hungry madman before Dr Who managed to re-freeze them. One advantage they have over Daleks is that they were slightly more humanoid, although just as war-like. Their little robot accomplices, the Cybermats, would make ideal Royal corgi replacements. *Royal suitability rating: 7.*

The Yeti. Another robot monster, Yetis were created by an alien intelligence who were trying to establish a foothold on Earth using the body of the High Lama, in 1930s Tibet. Fortunately, the Doctor was able to force the alien

A Cyberman yesterday

intelligence back onto an astral plane. Yetis were furry, with shiney metal bollocks, and had a good knowledge of the London underground. But there could be constitutional problems involved in trying to install a big hairy robot as Queen. *Royal suitability rating: 3.*

Ice Warriors were not robots, but Martians, and they attempted to take over the world after one had been de-frosted in a glacier. A sort of cross between Wurzel Gummage and a crocodile, their tendancy to try and destroy the world would preclude them from being Royal candidates. Another problem is that they talk with a slow hissing voice, and couldn't do good speeches. *Royal suitability rating: 2.*

Sea Devils may be surprise candidates for the throne as, like the Windsor's they have strong nautical links.

Dressed in fishing nets, and carrying torches, these reptile monsters had gone into hibernation because of the Moon or something, then woke up and decided to take over the world. Would no doubt be in favour of re-commissioning the Royal yacht. *Royal suitability rating: 6.*

We rang Buckingham Palace and asked which Doctor Who monster was the Queen's favourite, but the Queen's Press Secretary was unable to get back to us in time for our publishing deadline.

Second Royal bombshell

CURSE OF THE DALEKS

The growing Royal constitutional crisis took yet another unexpected twist yesterday when former stars of TV's Doctor Who admitted they were living in fear of their lives.

For a dreadful curse has hit the cast of the sixties Dr Who cinema movie 'Invasion of the Daleks 2065 A.D.' Since the big screen version of the popular long-running TV show was made almost thirty years ago, no less than *two* of the cast have mysteriously died. And remaining cast members have been left living in fear of dying as well.

SUPERSMAN

The showbusiness world has been holding its breath since actor Peter Cushing, who played the Doctor on the big screen, mysteriously died of old age recently. His death was closely followed by the tragic demise of cancer victim Roy Castle in equally mysterious circumstances. Actor and all-round entertainer Castle, who had fought a brave battle against his incurable condition, played Cushing's assistant in the film.

CAPTAINS FANSTATICS

And the double death blow leaves actor Bernard Cribbins, who also played the Doctor's assistant, in a second screen version of the popular science fiction series, in fear of his life.

WEB

And the web of terror began to spread yesterday with actress Jenny Agutter, who played alongside Cribbins in the screen version of 'The Railway Children', also fearing for her life in a knock-on effect star fear knee-jerk reaction. And the terror ripples spread even further across the showbusiness pond last night when comic

Former stars 'fear for their lives'

Rik Mayall, who played a bit part in the movie 'American Werewolf in London', which starred sexy Agutter in a no-holds-barred nude shower sex romp scene, admitted that he too fears he may fall victim to the Doctor Who domino effect showbusiness death curse mystery.

DWIGHT

Former 'Carry On' comic Bernard Bresslaw, who played an Ice Warrior in the popular long-running small screen version of the popular big screen sci-fi adventures was yesterday said to be 'alive' but unavailable for comment.

SUMNER

Meanwhile, the BBC remained tight-lipped over suggestions that the Spiders from Metibilus Three may be behind the growing showbusiness 'web of fear'. The Spiders from Metibilus Three, which appeared when people sat in a circle and went "om" several times, are thought to be so powerful that they made former Doctor Who actor Jon Pertwee turn into fellow star Tom Baker. Buckingham Palace officials were last night monitoring developments closely.

Design a Royal Doctor Who and the Daleks stamp

Buckingham Palace have asked us if you, our readers, could design a brand new postage stamp for when the Queen is made into a Dalek.

Designs must be based on the theme of Doctor Who, whilst also reflecting the majesty of our Royal family, and the deadly menace of the Daleks. They should be sent to 'Royal Dalek Stamps' at our usual address. But hurry. Your designs must be received by page 42 at the latest, as the winning entries will be published there.

*All designs submitted will become Crown Copyright. The Queen and The Bank of England reserve the right to use them on money as well.

LETTERBOCKS

Yule love this page, stuffed with onions and sage!

Viz Letterbocks
P.O. Bocks 1PT
Newcastle upon Tyne
NE99 1PT

Scotch poppycock

I read your feature on 'Britain's 100 Biggest Cocks' (issue 68) with some interest. I am convinced you have included Fish (out of Marillion) by mistake. As you can see from the enclosed photograph, he may have balls like Buster Gonad, but there is no sign of Derek's Dick.

A. Fan

*Anyone else who has photographs of naked Scottish pop stars holding their privates can win a fiver by sending them to 'Och! Top of the Jock Pop Cock and Plums' at the usual 'Letterbocks' address. If you want your photos back its probably best if you don't send them in the first place.

I found a monthly travel card for London zones 1, 2 and 3, together with the enclosed photograph on the No.141 bus last Monday. The card runs out on the 28th, and if the gentleman recognises himself perhaps he could send me a S.A.E. and I will return it as quickly as possible.

Miss S. Glover
Tottenham

*Thankyou Miss Glover. If the gentleman in question happens to be reading, may we suggest he writes to us and we will pass on his S.A.E. to Miss Glover. In the meantime, perhaps any London bus drivers who are reading this could cut out the above picture and stick it in their cab. If they see this person could they let him on the bus free of charge (in zones 1, 2 and 3) as he does have a travel card (valid until the 28th) but lost it on the No. 141 bus last Monday.

In response to D.S. Jackson and D.C. Cobham's letter (Letterbocks, this issue). My name is Fran Blake, which is very nearly a spoonerism of Bran Flakes. However, I am unemployed at present, and in any case my favourite breakfast cereal is Honey Nut Loops.

Fran Blake
Stow-on-the-Wold

Slippers slip up slip up

Miss N. Picker (issue 68) is only marginally more literate than her local Berwick market traders. "Slipper's £1.99" does *not* imply that the slippers own £1.99, but rather that one particular slipper owns £1.99, as the apostrophe is placed after the singular noun. If the money in question is indeed owned by more than one slipper, then the tatty fluorescent sign ought to read, "Slippers' £1.99".

With such confusion over the personal wealth of the town's footwear, it is no wonder Berwick is such a pigs' toilet.

May Q. Heave
Llanelli, Dyfed

With regard to the gentleman who lost his travel card and whose photograph appeared on the letters page (this issue). I was wondering if he'd be interested in going out one evening, for a meal perhaps, or maybe just a drink. I wondered if Miss Glover, or any bus drivers who speak to him, could pass on a message and ask if he'd be available one night next week. Any night except Thursday. I always feel a bit awkward making the first move, so perhaps he could write in and suggest a time and a place we could meet up.

Miss P. Green
Harlow

Writing on The Wall

"We don't need no education", Pink Floyd told us in 1979. I heartily agreed with my pop idols, and decided to pay no attention in metalwork. Fifteen years later I got a job – erecting the seating at their Earls Court concert.

It only goes to show, doesn't it.

T. Stephenson
Edgeware

Mick Hucknall recently sang, "Money's too tight to mention". He then went on to say that he, "Don't even qualify for. his pension". I note that Mr Hucknall is at present residing overseas, and it may therefore be possible for him to maintain his entitlement to a British Retirement Pension by paying voluntary class 3 National Insurance contributions during his absence, or, in the case of EEC nations, by participating in a reciprocal state pension scheme in his country of residence. For more information he should obtain leaflet NI48 which outlines the National Insurance position of persons living or working abroad. This can be obtained from most social security offices, or by writing to the D.S.S., Overseas Branch, Central Office, Newcastle upon Tyne, NE99.

Mrs M. Burn
Room A1301
D.S.S. Central Office

My life has been revolutionised by the invention of these 'widgets' which breweries now place inside draught beer cans. Gone are the days when I would have to drop a can of beer in the street, or shake it vigorously for several minutes before opening. Now all I have to do is pull the ring and hey presto! My clothes, carpet and furniture are showered with half a tin of frothing beer.

P. Allen
Newport, Shrops.

Falling off the wall

Imagine my surprise last night when I was awoken from my slumber by Cindy Crawford, who proceeded to lay on top of me, wearing only skimpy panties, and press her breasts into my face. I was in heaven, and simply could not believe my luck. Until a few seconds later, when I realised that it was only a *poster* of Cindy Crawford. The Blue Tac had come loose and it had fallen off my bedroom wall and landed on me. My only consolation is that I can now tell friends about the night Cindy Crawford fell for me!

Matt Sutcliffe
Halifax

P.S. Oh yes. And afterwards I had a good wank on the strength of the experience.

We are police vice squad officers, that is to say *porn cops,* and our favourite breakfast cereal is *Corn Pops*. Do any other readers have favourite breakfast cereals that are spoonerisms of their occupation?

D.S. Jackson
and D.C. Cobham.
Thames Valley C.I.D.

Recently I read that Claudia Schiffer wants to have *seventeen* children with her bungling magician boyfriend David Copperfield. How on Earth can she justify this? Surely it would be much fairer to let seventeen different blokes shag her.

Tony Fisher
Ipswich

They say you can't trust anybody these days. Sadly it is true. Only yesterday I broke into my next door neighbour's, stole his telly and smashed up his house while he was out shopping.

Steven Arthurs
Bristol

Badjoke

I thought this photograph of someone letting-off in a street called 'Badfart' in Denmark might be about the right level of humour required to amuse what remains of your readership.

Mr B. Burp
Surrey

HOLIDAYMAKERS.

Avoid the need to pack bulky shampoo bottles, which can leak in your suitcase, by arranging for the whole family to have 'skinhead' haircuts a day or two before departure.

Roger Plynth
Polegate

FUN-sized Mars bars make ideal normal-sized Mars bars, for dwarfs.

T. Bell
Southampton

MAKE a miniature 'mouse trap' for flies by using a spring-loaded wooden clothes peg, baited with a winnit.

T. Hawthorns
West Bromwich

PLASTIC tops from Smartie tubes make ideal frisbees for a pet gerbil, or hamster.

Eric Waspbottom
Nottingham

GARDENERS. Wrap seedling potatoes in a wire mesh before planting. Hey presto! Ready cut chips at harvest time.

Basil Pigsfanny
Nottingham

BEER bottle tops floated upside down in the bath, make ideal 'dinghies' for spiders. Flies can also use them as aircraft carriers.

M. Harwood
Yeadon

TOP TiPS

KING-sized Mars bars make ideal normal-sized Mars bars, for giants.

T. Dell
Southampton

PRETEND you're a giant panda by giving yourself two black eyes, eating bamboo shoots and refusing to have sex with your wife.

Mrs Di Unetic
Hong Kong

A GOOD book with all the pages covered in cellophane makes for ideal reading in the shower.

S. Adam
London

BEE keepers. Keep bee hives in strawberry fields to get jam instead of honey.

D. Unwin
Highgate

KEEP monkeys out of your kitchen by hiding bananas on top of a wardrobe in your bedroom.

Mrs D.
Includes–Underlay
Andfitting

NORMAL-sized Mars bars make ideal king-sized Mars bars for dwarfs, as well as fun-sized ones for giants.

T. Dell
Southampton

STAR Trek security officers. If you have never appeared in the programme before and suddenly Captain Kirk asks you to join a landing party beaming down to a planet surface, make an excuse. Do not go, as if you do invariably you will be killed.

T. Hooper
Bristol

OLD folks. Foil the VAT man this winter by clambering up on top of a bookcase, cupboard or wardrobe. Warm air rises, and so the temperature will increase the higher you climb.

B. Park
Oldham

CITY gents. Simulate the thrills of ski jumping by leaning forward and placing your umbrella under your arm next time you go down an escalator.

Matty
Liverpool

PEOPLE whose surname is Toblerone should always take along an empty 'Toblerone' chocolate box when attending interviews for office jobs. This would save your potential employer the expensive of having to make a name triangle for your desk, and therefore increase your changes of getting the job.

Mike Haworth
Crumpsall, Manchester

PRETEND your house is a pub by stubbing out cigarettes on the carpet, watering your cans of beer and kicking your wife out into the garden at 11.30.

Dave Upton
Hereford

SAVE money on expensive tickets to 'open air festivals' next summer. Simply put up a tent in your own back garden, piss up the side of it, and steal your own shoes.

Simone Glover
Tottenham N15

Donner unt blitzen

After reading your November issue I must write to tell you, "BOLLOCKS!" Your translation of 'Bolton' as if it should mean in German 'shitty arsehole' definitely not! I am here in England since half year for work, but am originally from Cologne/Germany. The real German translation of 'shitty arsehole' is *beschissenes arschloch*. But the thing which made me really crazy was the picture of a guy wearing a Nazi symbol. *Fuck off!* No Germans wear this.

In future contact me for German translations. Take it easy.

Marcus Dorff
Clapham SW12

HMM. HOW AM I GOING TO SMOOTHE THIS PIECE OF WOOD?

BOSS! THE PLANE! THE PLANE!

Commons split over Glenda's love kipper

A leading Labour MP's quim was at the centre of a political storm last night.

Conservative back bencher Sir Anthony Regents-Park yesterday launched an unprecedented attack on opposition member Glenda Jackson's bush. The outspoken member for Fulchester Sunnyoak rounded on Miss Jackson's pubes during Prime Minister's question time, describing them as a "threadbare snatch" and claiming that their appearance was a disgrace to British parliamentary tradition.

Sir Anthony yesterday

OSCAR

"Flaunting a tatty twat to all and sundry does not uphold the best traditions of this House", he said, referring to a film in which the Oscar winning former actress had appeared nude. "What will the Right Honourable Member sink to next? Hamburger shots?" he asked. There was uproar in the House, and after several moments the Speaker ruled that questions relating to a specific member's fadge were not within the scope of Parliamentary debate.

However, Mr Regents-Park continued his criticism afterwards. Referring to a film called 'The Music Lovers' he described a scene in which Jackson's pubic hair was clearly visible. "You saw it on a train I seem to recall. I have only seen the film once, and once was quite enough. It was quite the scraggiest stoat I have ever seen. It looked like Bob Geldof's moustache, stuck on vertically. Not that the appearance of Miss Jackson's kipper is at question here. Miss Jackson is entitled to have any array of pubic hair she likes. Indeed, she could have none at all if it suits her. That is not the issue. I am merely expressing the widely held view that an MP's muff should remain in her Parliamentary briefs, and not be paraded on cinema screens for the benefit of the dirty mac brigade".

KIM

"Look at Mrs Thatcher. In the eleven years that she was Prime Minister not once did she reveal her beef curtains. And rightly so. When she left office Britain's standing in the world had never been higher. Put simply, hairy pies and politics do not mix".

MARTY

This morning a storm was brewing over Mr Regents-Park's remarks. However, the 55 year old MP was unavailable for further comment, having been admitted to a private clinic after breaking an ankle falling from a step ladder whilst reaching for oranges on a top shelf in the kitchen of his West London batchelor home late last night.

106

BASED ON A TRUE STORY

Christmas 1987. At around 8.15pm on Thursday 24th December, 72 year old Edward Wilson died alone at his home in Thornaby, Cleveland, the victim of hypothermia.

Ten days later the fairy lights on his Christmas tree failed. After two months 'Ping!' The light bulb went. A fortnight later and the standard lamp conked out too.

Six months on and a fuse in Mr Wilson's fridge blew. The contents, already green with mould, began to stink. Not long afterwards mice gnawing at the wires rendered the telephone inoperative. After ten months the doorbell batteries ran flat. And twelve months after his death even Mr Wilson's wristwatch had ground to a halt.

But FOUR YEARS later, long after the maggots had picked him dry, Mr Wilson's **SAMSUN** TV was still working. And as the police officers who found the body discovered, the colour was still as bright as ever.

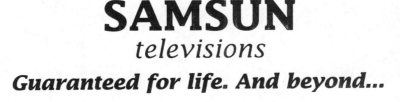

SAMSUN
televisions

Guaranteed for life. And beyond...

Peter Pan of Pop in Euro Song cash bribe sensation!

RICHARD THE TURD!

A bribery scandal is set to rock the British music industry to its foundations.

For we can exclusively reveal that squeaky clean pop singer Cliff Richard accepted cash bribes in order to 'throw' the Eurovision Song Contest.

And that will leave both friends and fans of the so-called 'Peter Pan of Pop' struggling to come to terms with the fact that their idol is in fact a **LIAR** and a **CHEAT**.

LIGHT

Richard's criminal activities came to light when we gave someone who once knew him £25,000 to make up the allegations. And we have compiled a damning dossier of evidence against the star, a copy of which is being sent to Top Of The Pops.

HEAT

In a video taped conversation the fifty-year-old bachelor star admitted singing badly in order to **LOSE** the 1973 Eurovision Song Contest. Richard was red hot favourite to win with Britain's entry 'Power to all our friends'. But TV viewers were stunned when the song failed to win enough votes, and the French entry 'Bing a bong a bang a boom' topped the poll.

KINETIC

On our tape, Richard is seen boasting to a pal about how he threw the result. "I sang it badly, and when I danced I kept my hips slightly out of tune with the rhythm", he said. "I got £75,000 grand for that. Not a bad result, eh?" he added.

Cheat Cliff is a liar and a fraud

Richard explained how he had been approached during the Second World War in an Egyptian night club by a mysterious gentleman wearing a red fez who offered him cash to lose the competition. "He said he represented a shady Far Eastern gambling syndicate who were planning to bet £100 million on me not winning. He gave me a brown envelope with £2 million in it, and said I'd get the rest when I didn't win".

POTENTIAL

Shady Far Eastern gambling syndicates can make hundreds of thousands of millions of pounds by betting on someone not winning the Eurovision Song Contest. By betting £100 at odds of 25 million to one, a shady Far Eastern gambling syndicate can stand to make £2.5 billion. And with such huge sums at stake the scandal is bound to spread throughout the pop world.

GLUCOSE

Already there are rumours that stars appearing on Top Of The Pops have accepted

Gift - cash for cartwheel

bribes from shady Far Eastern gambling syndicates. Roland Gift, lead singer with The Fine Young Cannibals, was investigated by the police after performing a cartwheel on the show in 1987. A dark haired man with sun glasses and a trilby hat entered a Far Eastern betting shop the day before and bet £50 on Gift performing a cartwheel on the show, at odds of 4000 to one. However, as a spokesman for Ladbrokes explained, the bet was not successful.

Greedy Cliff (left) caught on camera in an Egyptian nightclub accepting a million pounds. In a hat.

"Unfortunately for the shady Far Eastern gambling syndicate concerned the bet was only half of a double 'yankee'. They had also wagered that on the same programme Peter Powell would set light to one of his own farts with a match".

SILVER SPOON

If Powell had done so the mystery syndicate stood to have won over half the money in the world. Last night Peter Powell was unavailable for comment. A spokesman for the BBC said they would have to examine video evidence of all of Cliff Richard's 110 chart hits, and watch his film 'Summer Holiday' next time it comes on the telly, before deciding whether to press charges against the star.

Peter Pan couldn't get a pan handle

A former school pal of pop traitor Cliff Richard yesterday told reporters that the 52 year old virgin was no good in bed, and regularly two-timed his wife.

"I slept with him several times, and he was a selfish lover", she told us. "He may be the Peter Pan of pop, but he's certainly no Pinocchio when it comes to pan handles," she added.

A prostitute yesterday

SORDID

The seventeen year old girl, who asked not to be named, mentioned that Richard was also a **bully** and **thief**. "He would often steal the other kids' dinner money, mug old age pensioners and kill people's pets with fireworks," she added.

Good news for trees

There was good news for trees this week when the Government announced that there will be no more paper by the year 2000.

And it will be good news for people having there breakfast too, as it will be an end to awkward-to-fold newspapers.

Late last night there was a reprieve for cardboard boxes. A motion to replace them with polystyrene packaging was defeated in the Commons by three votes to nil.

"TRAITOR!" – say former pals

By GREG TURD and NINA COW

Pals of 51 year old Richard yesterday queued up to condemn the disgraced singer.

JUDAS

"If this is true, I'd be most surprised," said Terry Wogan, who hosted the Eurovision Song Contest.

SHITBAG

Another former showbusiness buddy, actress Una Stubbs, was last night unavailable for comment.

Wogan - surprised

Are you a TRAMP or a TOFF?

THE LINE THAT CANNOT LIE

Hobo or Hooray Henry – how do YOU rate yourself? Would you be at home among the hob knobs of high society, or are you more of a meths drinking Harold Ramp?
None of us would admit to being either, but who are we fooling? Discover the REAL you by following the line of truth. Only by answering each question honestly will the true answer reveal itself.

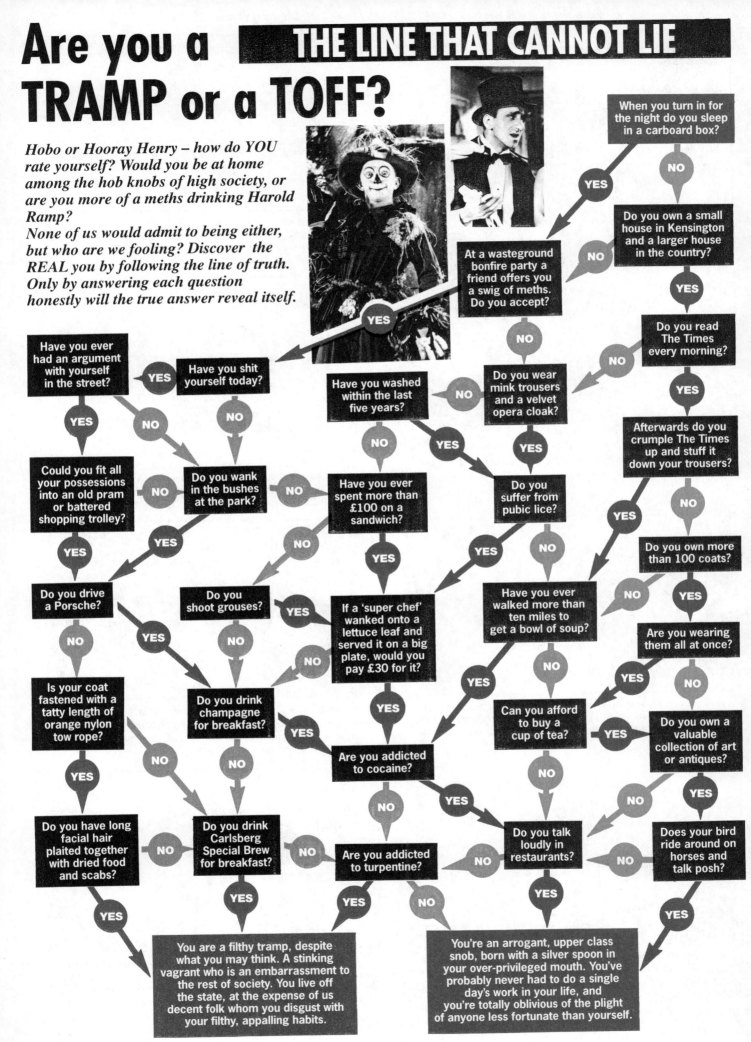

When you turn in for the night do you sleep in a carboard box?

At a wasteground bonfire party a friend offers you a swig of meths. Do you accept?

Do you own a small house in Kensington and a larger house in the country?

Do you read The Times every morning?

Have you ever had an argument with yourself in the street?

Have you shit yourself today?

Have you washed within the last five years?

Do you wear mink trousers and a velvet opera cloak?

Afterwards do you crumple The Times up and stuff it down your trousers?

Could you fit all your possessions into an old pram or battered shopping trolley?

Do you wank in the bushes at the park?

Have you ever spent more than £100 on a sandwich?

Do you suffer from pubic lice?

Do you own more than 100 coats?

Do you drive a Porsche?

Do you shoot grouses?

If a 'super chef' wanked onto a lettuce leaf and served it on a big plate, would you pay £30 for it?

Have you ever walked more than ten miles to get a bowl of soup?

Are you wearing them all at once?

Is your coat fastened with a tatty length of orange nylon tow rope?

Do you drink champagne for breakfast?

Are you addicted to cocaine?

Can you afford to buy a cup of tea?

Do you own a valuable collection of art or antiques?

Do you have long facial hair plaited together with dried food and scabs?

Do you drink Carlsberg Special Brew for breakfast?

Are you addicted to turpentine?

Do you talk loudly in restaurants?

Does your bird ride around on horses and talk posh?

You are a filthy tramp, despite what you may think. A stinking vagrant who is an embarrassment to the rest of society. You live off the state, at the expense of us decent folk whom you disgust with your filthy, appalling habits.

You're an arrogant, upper class snob, born with a silver spoon in your over-privileged mouth. You've probably never had to do a single day's work in your life, and you're totally oblivious of the plight of anyone less fortunate than yourself.

111

Shane McDougall
THE
Kilted Cowboy
of
Kilmarnock

*featuring Aberdeen Angus,
his mighty clockwork elephant of steel.*

The braw bonnie wee Scottish village of Glencampbell, nestling in the foothills of the Cairngorms, had once been home to a thriving shortbread industry, and boasted the largest shortbread distillery in the highlands.

But the shortbread kilns stand cold and idle, and the tartan tins stacked outside the distillery remain empty. For the town was plagued by a ruthless band of shortbread thieves – the Pogoing Pirates of Penzance.

Every year at harvest-time the black-hearted Cornish brigands would sail their inland ship down the cobbled High Street, and boarding parties of bouncing cut throats would terrorise the helpless townsfolk.

They would mercilessly pillage the entire year's harvest of all butter shortbread, petticoat and finger biscuits alike, and any man who dared resist them was forced to space hopper the plank, into a bushy clump of thistles.

The desperate villagers called an emergency meeting to discuss their predicament. "What can we do? We're no match for those pirates and their pogo sticks", said the Mayor. But one brave laddie was prepared to speak up.

"We cannot fight these pirates alone", said wee Hamish Dunn, the vet's son. "We must send for help". "But how?" asked the Mayor. "I could tattoo a message onto wee Tam my pet salmon", said Hamish. "He can swim for help".

The people of Glencampbell realised that the frail fish was their only hope. They looked on anxiously as wee Hamish began to spell out the townsfolk's desperate plea for help on the side of the brave wee salmon.

Then the bold wee laddie released the plucky fish into the river. "I only hope it has the strength to swim upstream and find somebody who can help us", said the Mayor. "Good luck wee Tam", said Hamish.

For countless days and nights the plucky pink fish battled upstream, jumping waterfalls, climbing weirs, fording streams and trekking miles o'er hill and dale, till at long last it reached the top of Ben Nevis.

On top of the mountain a lonesome figure and his elephant were fishing. "Why, what's this Angus? Shucks! Looks like I've caught us a wee pink fishy. This'll dee mighty fine for ma tea, wi', ma tatties an' ma neeps, pardner".

With a series of clumsy blows to the head from the butt of his Colt 45, the six shootin' Scotsman bludgeoned the bonnie wee fish into oblivion. "Tek that, y'low down son of a bitch cotton pickin' varmint", he whooped.

But as the wee fishy sizzled in his chuck tin, the Kilted Cowboy noticed something out of the ordinary. "Hoots! That sure is the darndest thing. There's some sort of message tattooed on the side of ma fish".

"Well, I'll be a son of gun the noo!" cried the Kilted Cowboy. "Someone must be in trouble". Hamish Dunn's tattooed message read bold and clear. And Shane McDougall realised that someone, somewhere needed his help.

And so the Kilted Cowboy packed his bags, wound up his mighty clockwork steed of steel and bravely set off across the bonnie Scottish hills in search of adventure and the unknown dangers which lay ahead.

BRITAIN'S 100 BIGGEST COCKS

Who has the biggest parts? Michael Caine or Roger Moore? How much have the stars got tucked away in their trousers? Who is packing the biggest packet?

Britain's 100 Biggest Cocks is the most eagerly awaited chart of the year. Published annually, it provides the definitive guide to whose cock is bigger than whose.

There are few surprises in this year's listings. One notable new entry is footballer Ryan Giggs, who only just started to use his cock recently, and appears in 80th position with a respectable four and half inches. Absent from the Top 100 for the first time since 1963 is Prince Charles, whose asset has been affected by adverse publicity and the break-up of his marriage.

REED...*Biggest prick in Britain*

1	**Oliver Reed** Film actor and drunkard	22½"
2	**Viscount William Whitelaw** Former Home Secretary	18"
3	**Bob Hoskins** Film actor	17¼"
4	**John Prescott** Labour MP for Hull	17"
5	**Peter Carter-Ruck QC** Top libel lawyer	16½"
6	**Bernie Grant** Labour MP for Tottenham	16¼"
7	**Patrick Moore** Astrologer	16"
8	**Tony Knowles** Snooker player	15"

9	**Fish out of Marillion** Lead singer out of Marillion	15"
10	**Chas Chandler** Pop entrepreneur and former Animal	14½"
11	**Jack Walker** Blackburn Rovers chairman and crisp magnate	14"
12	**Tom Farmer** Kwikfit chairman	14"
13	**Michael Caine** Film actor and restauranteur	13½"
14	**Lord Lichfield** Society photographer	12¼"
15	**Bernard Matthews** Norfolk turkey farmer	12"
16	**Andrew Lloyd-Webber** Composer	12"
17	**General Sir Peter de la Billiere** British Forces chief	11½"
18	**Nigel Mansell** Motor racing driver	11"
19	**Captain Birdseye** Frozen fish finger magnate	10½"
20	**Eddie Stobart Jnr.** Road haulage contractor	10"

EVERETT...*Big twat, little cock*

21	**Len Ganley** Snooker referee	9½"
22	**Don Estelle** Actor	9½"
23	**Sir Joseph Bazooka** Bubble gum magnate	9"
24	**Tony Adams** Footballer	8½"
25	**Malcolm Hardy** Comedian and club owner	8"

| 76 | **Tony Jacklin** Golfer | 5¼" |
| 77 | **Sir Terence Conran** Restauranteur and businessman | 5" |

WYMAN...*No satisfaction with 5"*

78	**Bill Wyman** Former Rolling Stone	5"
79	**Sir Henry Bic** Inventor of the Biro pen	5"
80	**Ryan Giggs** Footballer	4½"
81	**HRH The Duke of Edinburgh** Queen's husband	4½"
82	**Roger Moore** Film actor	4¼"
83	**Ian Wright** Footballer	4"

84	**Jonathon Ross** Television presenter	3¼"
85	**Russell Grant** Astronomer	3"
86	**Jimmy Nail** Actor, writer, producer, director, cameraman	2½"
87	**Hugh Grant** Actor	2½"
88	**Marco-Pierre White** Jumped up long haired cook	1½"
89	**Anita Roddick** Body Shop owner	1½"
90	**Ian Hislop** Private Eye editor and broadcaster	1¼"
91	**Michael Winner** Opinionated film director	1"
92	**David Sullivan** Stumpy porn publisher	1"
93	**Bruiser de Cadanet** Twat	1"
94	**Rupert Everett** Bigger Twat	1"
95	**Matthew Corbett** Former Sooty presenter	1"
96	**Simon Mayo** Radio One breakfast DJ	½"
97	**Gary Bushell** Sun journalist	½"
98	**Brian Harvey** Singer out of East 17	½"
99	**Piers Morgan** News of the World editor	½"
100	**Dennis Wise** Footballer	¼"

WISE...*Sweet F.A. for a cock*

All measurements are length in inches, 'on the soft'. Whilst figures cannot be taken as a precise measurement, they have been compiled using all relevant information available to us, and can be considered to give a fair indication of who's got the biggest cock. For reasons of space only the top 25 and bottom 25 names have been included.

KNOWLES...*Lines up a long pink*

PATRICK...*'Moore' than meets the eye*

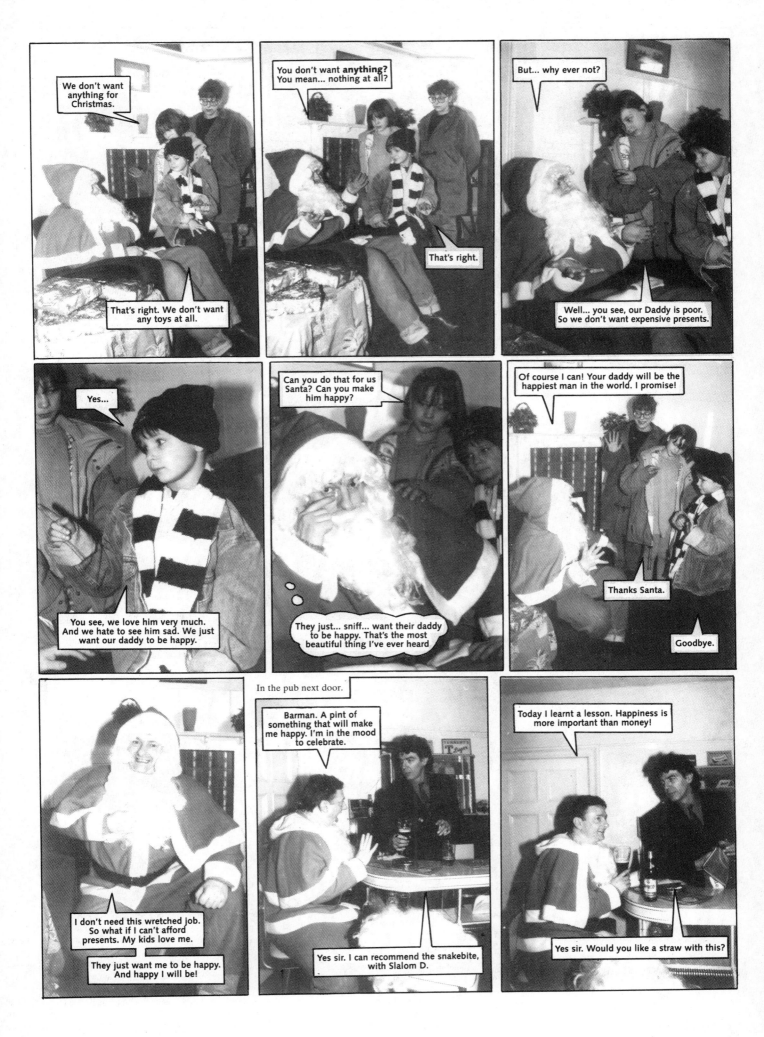

Continues on page 123.

Are the squares hassling you for bread?

Hey. Chill out.

If there's one thing you don't need at college, it's hassle. Like the landlord causing a heavy scene about the rent. Or you've checked out a groovy pair of strides in a hip boutique, but you ain't got no moolar to buy them with. And you can't do your homework, cos you used your last sheet of paper rolling up a bong to smoke happy baccy.

On top of all these problems the last thing you need is a wrinkly dude bank manager who hassles you the minute your account goes a couple of 'K' O.D.

At Berkleys we understand about student life. All of our managers used to be students back in the thirties. We know that you need more than pens, pencils and protractors to see you through the term. You also need chewing gum, pop records, cinema tickets and fizzy drinks. And after a hard day's work you wanna hang out with the other cats in the Union bar, or maybe buy tickets to see the latest pop group.

At Berkleys, that's cool. Our staff are all hip to the jive, daddy oh. And we aren't going to lay some heavy guilt trip on you just cos you go a couple of grand into the red. Like, big deal. It's only bread, yeah? At your local branch you'll find all of our staff are hip cats, just like you. In fact, don't be surprised if you see our Student Advice Officer in the local record shop checking out the latest sounds. So why not come and check **us** out, or complete the coupon below and collect a free* pencil sharpener, Biro pen and a packet of chewing gum.

Come into our parlour…

Berkleys Student Bank Account   (Complete coupon in BLOCK CAPITALS)

Dear Mr Spider,
I am a fly. Please may I come into your parlour. Send me details of Berkleys Student Accounts.

Name .... Address..

.... Post code............................

GAMES WANKER REVIEWS

with Joe Foureyes, aged 11.

GAMEPLAN

FRESH AIR QUEST
(MEGA TOSS – £85.95)

Games masters everywhere prepare to meet your match. This is the finest action/adventure game ever to hit your console, and guaranteed to keep you awake for weeks. First stage is to escape from the MIGHTY SO-FA, then negotiate the GREAT DOOR OF BED-ROOM and pass into the KINGDOM OF LAN-DING.
The second stage features even more thrilling gameplay. The aim to descend the MIGHTY CASE OF STAIR until you reach the OUTER DOOR. This is where the action hots up as players must now open the mystic and powerful MIGHTY LATCH OF YALE. The highlights of this fabulous game is when you crack the lock and stagger out, blinking, into the sunshine.

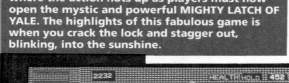

THE HYGIENATOR
(HOOVER – £79.95)

The aim of the game is to escape from the evil Hygienator who's aim is to remove your filthy clothing, scrub your spotty face, and wash your lank, greasy hair. *Tip:* Look out for Hygienator's deadly companion SOAPAN WATER and his DEODORANT BLASTER. To get to Level 2 you must go for 18 weeks without a bath.

EPILEPTOR 7
(SHITA CD – £89.95)

I rate this game better even than EPILEPTOR 6 which I also bought for £89.95 three days ago and only got as far as Level 3 before collapsing in a fit. The graphics are out of this world, with non-stop beeping and flashing reminiscent of the awe-inspiring CONVULSATRON (AGA – £120.95) which killed my brother after 74 hours of non-stop gameplay. If it's excitement you want, the positively life-threatening EPILEPTOR 7 is a must for your console.

WALLET MEGA BLASTER
(ELECTROLUX – £210.95)

WALLET MEGA BLASTER supercedes WALLET BLASTER which came out last week at only £129.95. The new game, at a mega improved £210.95, is not compatible with anything, so you'll also need the new WALLET MEGA BLASTER console at £399.95. Also, tell mum to look out for SUPER HYPER WALLET MEGA BLASTER in the shops next week for a sensational £799.95.

DINNER NIGHTMARE
(LEVER BROS. – £79.95)

This is the toughest challenge of all. I struggled to get onto Level 3 after a solid month of non-stop gameplay. The aim is to sit and have a meal with the rest of your family, and to make conversation with them. *Skill rating:* Virtually impossible.

MASTURBATOR III
(BLACK AND DEKKER – £79.95)

This is a straightforward game for beginners. Static picture format. The beautiful semi-naked PRINCESS ORGASMA appears on the screen surrounded by dragons, snakes, wizards etc. Your task is to put down the joystick, pick up your cock, and have a wank. But beware the MIGHTY MUTH-OR who can enter your bedroom at any time and catch you pulling your pud.

Dear Joe

I am stuck at Level 1 of FART SACK (MORPHY RICHARDS – £90.99). How do I get out of bed and put my clothes on?
D.C., Walthamstow

Set ALARM on bedside table before entering SLEEP mode. When bell rings lift head to VERTICAL position and get UP. The secret is then to move curtains to OPEN and locate clothes.

Dear Joe

I have been stuck at Level 17 of SAD WANKER (Tate & Lyall) since Christmas 1991. I have lost the use of my eyes and my skin is the colour of porridge. How do I get out of this game?
D.S., Reading

Go to WALL. Locate the SOCKET. Pull PLUG until it comes OUT.

HOUSE SEARCH
(IDEAL MEXICO – £54.95)

Adventure unfolds in this exciting quest to locate your family. Behind the many doors of your house could be brothers, sisters, a mother and a father. Go through the house, room by room, locating as many people as you can, and saying "hello" to them. If you haven't met before, introduce yourself. An exciting journey into the unknown.

Dear Joe

I have reached Level 6 of SAD WANKER (SPEAR & JACKSON) and have managed to get out of the house, walk along the street, and find a girl. But I cannot enter into a conversation with her. How do I proceed to the next Level?
S.B., Hungerford

Simple. Pause game. Find a PUB. Enter and press REQUEST BEER. Repeat until you reach Level SLIGHTLY MERRY. Unpause game, approach girl and press TALK. You will then be armed with CAREFREE CONVERSATION, a mighty weapon. But beware the demon DIZZINESS, and the deadly THROWING UP down her blouse or PISSING your trousers.

Dear Joe

I got to the 10th Level of EPILEPTOR without a fit. Only mild nausea. How do I get to the 11th Critical Level.
H.C., Sunderland

Tip: Sit closer to the screen. Ideally it should be about six inches from your eyes. Turn brightness UP. Close curtains.

Dear Joe

I heard a friend of mine talk about GIRLS. What is GIRLS, and is it ATARI compatible? What is the highest score?
B.H., Hounslow

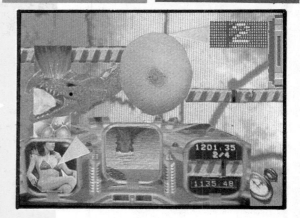